HOW T

by
E. A. Parr, B.Sc., C.Eng., M.I.E.E.

BERNARD BABANI (publishing) LTD
THE GRAMPIANS
SHEPHERDS BUSH ROAD
LONDON W6 7NF
ENGLAND

PLEASE NOTE

Although every care has been taken with the production of this book to ensure that any projects, designs, modifications and/or programs, etc., contained herewith, operate in a correct and safe manner and also that any components specified are normally available in Great Britain, the Publishers do not accept responsibility in any way for the failure, including fault in design, of any project, design, modification or program to work correctly or to cause damage to any other equipment that it may be connected to or used in conjunction with, or in respect of any other damage or injury that may be so caused, nor do the Publishers accept responsibility in any way for the failure to obtain specified components.

Notice is also given that if equipment that is still under warranty is modified in any way or used or connected with home-built equipment then that warranty may be void.

© 1982 BERNARD BABANI (publishing) LTD

First Published – April 1982
Reprinted – July 1986
Reprinted – July 1988
Reprinted – January 1990
Reprinted – October 1991
Reprinted – May 1993
Reprinted – January 1995
Reprinted – January 1997
Reprinted – June 1999

British Library Cataloguing in Publication Data:
Parr, E. A.
  How to use op amps – (BP88)
  1. Operational amplifiers
  2. Integrated circuits
  I. Title
  621.381'73'5   TK7871.58.06

ISBN 0 85934 063 5

Printed and bound in Great Britain by Cox & Wyman Ltd, Reading

CONTENTS

ACKNOWLEDGEMENTS

I would like to thank the editors of Practical Wireless and Electronics and Radio Constructor for permission to use material that appeared under my name in those magazines, and Texas Instruments and RS Components for freely given technical assistance and data sheets.

Finally, I would like to thank my wife, Alison, who, as ever, converted my illegible handwriting into readable typewritten text.

Andrew Parr
April 1982

CHAPTER 1
MEET THE OPERATIONAL AMPLIFIER

1.1 INTRODUCTION

The Operational Amplifier is probably the most versatile
circuit available to the electronics engineer. For a price similar
to a general purpose transistor, it is possible to purchase an
integrated circuit with several hundred "components", very
high gain and predictable performance. The Op Amp is thus a
basic building block for applications from audio to industrial
control.

To many people the terms Op Amp and 741 are interchange-
able, but in fact the 741 is merely the commonest member of
a whole family of devices. This book has been written as a
designers guide for most Operational Amplifiers, serving both
as a source book of circuits and a reference book for design
calculations. The approach has been made as non mathematical
as possible, and should be understandable by most amateurs.

1.2 DC AMPLIFIERS

The designers of DC amplifiers using discrete components face
a difficult task, and it is not difficult to see why. In Fig.1.1 we

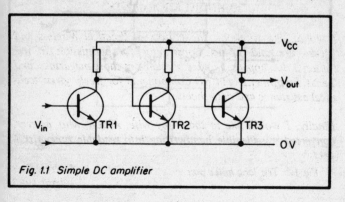

Fig. 1.1 Simple DC amplifier

1

have a simple DC amplifier, with an input signal V_{in} and output V_{out}. Unfortunately this circuit would make a reasonable thermometer but a very poor amplifier.

The first stage transistor, TR1, has characteristics which, like all transistors, are temperature dependent. The most important characteristics are the base emitter voltage V_{BE} which changes by 2mV per degree Centigrade, and the collector emitter leakage current which doubles for every 10°C. These effects will produce voltage changes at TR1's collector which are indistinguishable from voltage changes caused by V_{in}. Since DC amplifiers are used with input voltages of the order of a few millivolts, this state of affairs is obviously intolerable.

Most DC amplifiers are therefore built around the long tailed pair of Fig.1.2. TR1 and TR2 are identical transistors, maintained at the same temperature by a common heat sink. In an ideal circuit, TR1 and TR2 will suffer identical temperature changes in V_{BE} and I_{CEO}, which will exactly cancel and cause V_{out} to be dependent solely on V_{in}.

Even with matched transistors, designing a high gain DC

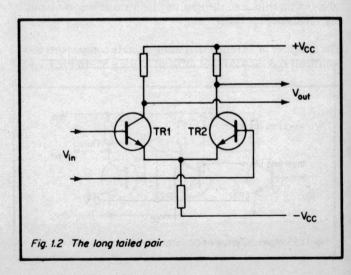

Fig. 1.2 The long tailed pair

amplifier takes a lot of careful work, but manufacturers were quick to realise that integrated circuits were ideal for the production of DC amplifiers. All the transistors on a chip have identical characteristics, and the small size ensures all components are at the same temperature. DC amplifiers can thus be made with very high gain and minimal temperature effects.

The first IC DC amplifier was the 709, introduced by Fairchild in the mid 1960s (On a personal note the author has a soft spot for the 709, it was the first IC I ever used, and the first I destroyed at a cost of £18 to my employer. The same chip today, 15 years later, costs 50p.) The 709 by today's standard has many shortcomings, and a whole family of amplifiers has been produced. The commonest is the 741 which has been described as the Universal Component.

A DC amplifier chip in its simplest form has just 6 connections summarised on Fig.1.3. The positive supply ($+V_{CC}$), negative supply ($-V_{CC}$) and the output are obvious. The amplifier has two inputs, denoted by + and −, corresponding to the two transistor bases on Fig.1.2. These are known, respectively, as the non inverting and the inverting inputs, and deserve some explanation.

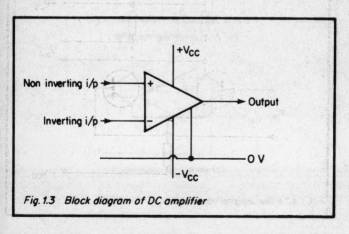

Fig. 1.3 Block diagram of DC amplifier

3

The amplifier amplifies the voltage between the two inputs. Let us assume, therefore, that the − input is connected to 0V and an input signal applied to the + input, as shown on Fig. 1.4a. It will be found that the output moves in the same sense as the input. If we reverse the input connections, and connect the signal to the − input, and the + input to 0V, as shown on Fig.1.4b, the output will move in the opposite sense to the input. The terms "inverting" and "non inverting" thus refer to the sense of the inputs with respect to the resulting output.

DC amplifiers are characterised by very high gains; 200,000 being typical for the common 741. Normally supplies of ±15V are used, so an input voltage of less than 1mV will cause the output to saturate. In practice, as we shall see, all DC amplifiers are invariably used with negative feedback which, in conjunction with high gains, gives very predictable results.

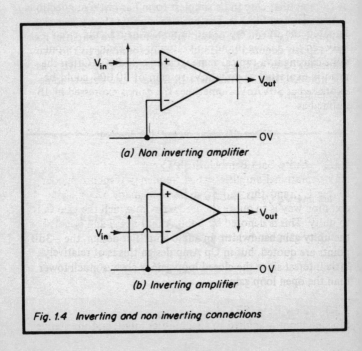

(a) Non inverting amplifier

(b) Inverting amplifier

Fig. 1.4 Inverting and non inverting connections

DC amplifiers are used in instrumentation, audio circuits, filter design and industrial control. They have become a universal component, and one particular amplifier, the 741, could possibly be the most successful and universally used chip ever made.

Early (non IC) DC amplifiers were once widely used in analog computers, and were called Operational Amplifiers. The name has become applied to all DC amplifiers, and in this book we use the shortened form Op Amp.

1.3 COMING TO TERMS WITH THE OP AMP

If we are to use Op Amps we must be able to select a suitable IC from the vast range available. Op Amps are described by a wide range of terms, which are explained below.

1.3.1 DC Gain (AVD)
Possibly the most important term, defined as the ratio between the change in output volts and the change in input volts causing it (a typical value would be 30,000). Often the ratio is expressed as volts/mV, so gain of 30,000 could be expressed as 30V/mV. Sometimes the gain is expressed in dB, defined as:—

$$AVD = 20.\log_{10} (V_{out}/V_{in}) \text{ decibels.}$$

1.3.2 Unity Gain Bandwidth (BW)
Any operational amplifier has a frequency response similar to Fig.1.5, and this can be defined in many ways. One common way is to quote the frequency at which the gain falls to unity. This is denoted by point A on Fig.1.5 and is called the unity gain bandwidth. In audio amplifier design, the -3dB points are quoted, but in Op Amp design this is of relatively little interest since the closed loop gain is always much lower than the open loop gain.

1.3.3 Slew Rate (SR)
If a step input is applied to an amplifier input, and the step is

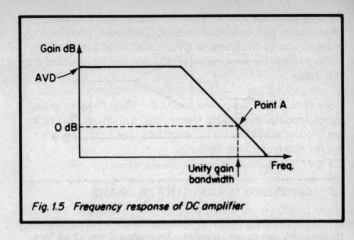

Fig. 1.5 Frequency response of DC amplifier

sufficient to drive the output to saturation, the output will change in a ramp form as Fig.1.6. The ramp slope is determined by the circuit of the amplifier, and is called the Slew Rate. A 741 has a slew rate of 1 volt/μs. High speed amplifiers have slew rates of the order of 100 volts/μs.

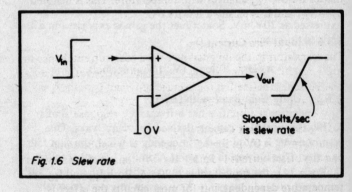

Fig. 1.6 Slew rate

1.3.4 Input Offset Voltage (V_IO)
In Fig.1.7 we show all the relevant input and output currents. Suppose $V_1 = V_2 = 0V$. In theory V_{out} will be zero, but in practice due to slight manufacturing tolerances V_{out} will be

6

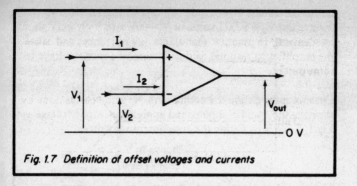

Fig. 1.7 Definition of offset voltages and currents

either positive or negative by a significant amount. If V_1 is slowly moved until V_{out} is zero, the difference between V_1 and V_2 is the input offset voltage. The figure for a 741 is around 2mV, quite small really.

1.3.5   Offset Voltage Temperature Coefficient ($\propto V_{IO}$)
In practice, V_{IO} is not particularly important since it can be nulled out by a zeroing potentiometer. What does usually matter is how V_{IO} changes with temperature. This is denoted by $\propto V_{IO}$ and is typically a few $\mu V/^\circ C$.

1.3.6   Input Bias Current (I_{IB})
The transistors in the long tail pair need base current, hence in Fig.1.7, with $V_1 = V_2 = 0V$, I_1 and I_2 will not be zero. The bias current is defined as the average of I_1 and I_2 with V_1 and V_2 both zero. A typical value for a 741 is $0.1\mu A$.

1.3.7   Input Offset Current (I_{IO})
With $V_1 = V_2 = 0V$ in Fig.1.7, I_1 and I_2 will not be equal, and the offset current is simply the difference between I_1 and I_2. For a 741, the typical value is 20mA. Both I_{IB} and I_{IO} are temperature dependent, but for most circuits the effect is negligible.

1.3.8   Common Mode Rejection Ratio (CMRR)
A perfect DC amplifier amplifies the voltage between the + and − inputs, and totally ignores the common mode voltage

on the terminals. The output voltages on Fig.1.7 with $V_1 =$ 9 volts and $V_2 = 9.001$ volts, or $V_1 = 0V$ and $V_2 = 1mV$ should be identical. In practice, manufacturing tolerances will cause the amplifier to respond to the 9V common mode voltage to some extent.

First we must define the common mode gain. This is done by shorting the + and − inputs, and applying an input voltage as Fig.1.8. We then define the common mode gain as :−

$$ACM = \frac{\text{change in } V_{out}}{\text{change in } V_{in}} .$$

The change in signal is used to avoid problems with V_{IO} defined above.

We have already defined the DC gain, AVD, in section 1.3.1. The Common Mode Rejection Ratio is then simply:−

$$CMRR = \frac{AVD}{ACM}$$

CMRR is normally very large, so it is convenient to express it in decibels. A 741 has a CMRR of 90dB.

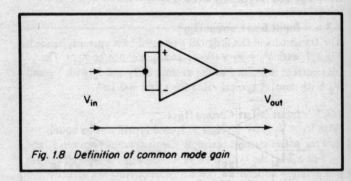

Fig. 1.8 Definition of common mode gain

1.4 STABILITY

An Op Amp has a frequency response that can, with some ICs,

8

give high gain at high frequencies. It is not particularly surprising to find many Op Amp circuits turn into Op Amp oscillators. There are many mathematical techniques to predict stability (Nyquist Diagrams, Bode plots to name but two) but these are beyond the scope of a book such as this. There are, fortunately, several empirical methods that can be used.

The first, and obvious, is not to use an amplifier that is too good for your application. Amplifiers such as the 741 have a strategically placed capacitor on the chip which causes the gain to roll off in a predictable manner. (The -3dB point on a 741 is as low as 10Hz, but the device still has useful gain at 40kHz, and unity gain at 1MHz). These devices are said to be unconditionally stable, and it is very unusual for a 741 and similar devices to misbehave.

If an unconditionally stable amplifier cannot be used, an Op Amp with compensation terminals should be substituted. These amplifiers have internal points within the circuit brought out so the user can shape the response. This can be done by two capacitors and a resistor as done on the 709 on Fig.1.9a or by a single capacitor as used by the 308 on Fig. 1.9b. Manufacturers data sheets give details of component values.

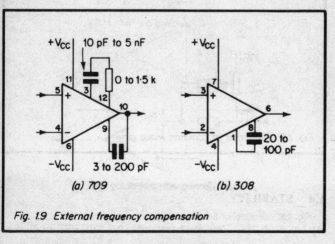

Fig. 1.9 External frequency compensation

1.5 ZEROING

In section 1.3.4 we saw that Op Amps have an input voltage offset of a few millivolts. In many low gain and AC applications this offset does not matter, but where a small voltage is to be amplified, the offset must be removed.

Many Op Amp ICs have internal zeroing points brought out to pins, typical being the 741 shown on Fig.1.10a. This allows the amplifier to be zeroed with one external potentiometer. As a cautionary note, shorting the zeroing pins to 0V or the positive supply is certain death for a 741.

An alternative method, useful for the inverting mode described

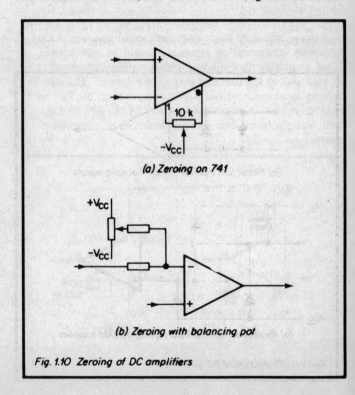

(a) Zeroing on 741

(b) Zeroing with balancing pot

Fig. 1.10 Zeroing of DC amplifiers

10

in section 2, is to add a balancing voltage by a potentiometer and resistor as Fig.1.10b. This method should be used where a precision amplifier is required even if zeroing pins are provided, because the resulting zero is more stable.

1.6 PROTECTION

Integrated circuit Op Amps are very well protected, and later versions are almost bullet proof. The 741 in particular seems immune to short circuits and will even stand reversed supplies and being plugged into a socket wrong way round!

Some Op Amps can be destroyed by a large voltage (above 5 volts) between their inputs. These amplifiers should be protected by diodes across the inputs as Fig.1.11a. In normal use the diodes do not conduct, and will not affect the circuit.

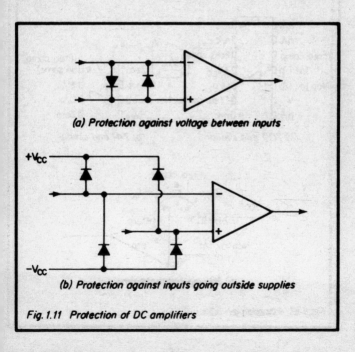

(a) Protection against voltage between inputs

(b) Protection against inputs going outside supplies

Fig. 1.11 Protection of DC amplifiers

11

Most Op Amps will be destroyed if an input goes outside the supply rails. If this is possible (remember Murphy's Law!) diodes should be added as Fig.1.11b.

FET Op Amps are vulnerable in the same way as CMOS, and normal precautions should be taken against static damage when using them.

1.7 PACKAGING

There is a remarkable degree of consistency in the packaging of Op Amps. The first Op Amp was the 709 shown on Fig. 1.12a. This configuration was carried forward to the 8 pin DIL packaging of the 741 shown on Fig.1.12b. It will be noted

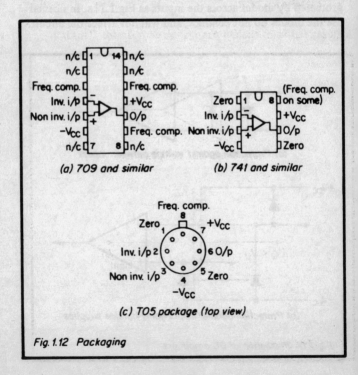

(a) 709 and similar

(b) 741 and similar

(c) TO5 package (top view)

Fig. 1.12 Packaging

that this is compatible with the 709, and has, in fact, been adopted as a standard.

Wherever possible, manufacturers have used 1.12b, with minor variations for individual functions (such as zeroing and compensation) on pins 1 and 8. Almost all Op Amps use the same pins for inputs, supplies and output. This simplifies designs considerably as a better specification (or cheaper) Op Amp can easily be substituted if the initial choice is wrong.

Early Op Amps used the 8 pin TO5 package of Fig.1.12c. This has been largely superceded by the DIL package, and should only be used on a replacement basis.

1.8 COMPARATORS

A close relative of the Op Amp is the comparator. This is a

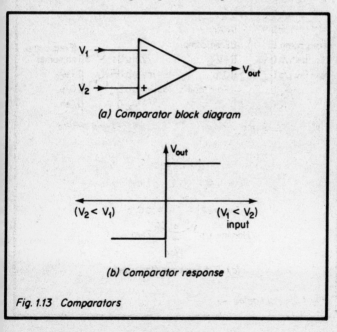

(a) Comparator block diagram

(b) Comparator response

Fig. 1.13 Comparators

high gain DC amplifier designed to compare the magnitude of its two inputs. It thus has the response of Fig.1.13b. Comparators are, however, designed for speed, and most will switch in around 100nS.

Comparators have offsets similar to Op Amps, and in general the terms of section 1.3 apply to comparators. A typical comparator is the LM311.

CHAPTER 2.
BASIC CIRCUITS

2.1 INTRODUCTION

This book describes many practical circuits using operational amplifiers. In this section the basic building block circuits are described, and the design principles are given. Although described for the 741, they can of course, be implemented with any operational amplifier.

2.2 INVERTING AMPLIFIER

2.2.1 Description

The classic operational amplifier circuit is the inverting amplifier shown on Fig.2.1. Since the amplifier has a very high gain, and the output is going to stay within the supply rails we can say that both of the input pins (2 and 3) are going to stay within a millivolt of 0V. For all practical purposes, therefore, we can say that the junction of R1 and R2 is at 0V. This is known as a Virtual Earth in the jargon, and simplifies the design considerably.

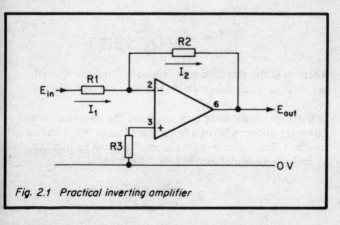

Fig. 2.1 Practical inverting amplifier

We can now work out I_1 easily, because:—

$$I_1 = \frac{E_{in}}{R1}.$$

Similarly, I_2 is given by:—

$$I_2 = \frac{E_{out}}{R2}.$$

Since $I_2 = -I_1$ we can write:—

$$\frac{E_{in}}{R1} = -\frac{E_{out}}{R2},$$

or

$$\frac{E_{out}}{E_{in}} = -\frac{R2}{R1}.$$

The minus sign denotes inversion (i.e. a positive input voltage gives a negative output voltage).

This is an interesting result, since the amplifier gain does not appear in the formula, and the gain is determined solely by R1 and R2!. This is, in fact, correct if the amplifier gain is very high and the closed loop gain relatively low. The full formula is:—

$$\frac{E_{out}}{E_{in}} = -\frac{R2}{R1 + (R2 + R1)/A}$$

where A is the amplifier gain (typically 20,000). For all practical purposes the $(R2 + R1)/A$ term can be neglected.

In the above analysis we have neglected the base bias currents. These are of the order of a few hundred nano Amps and cause an offset. The effect is normally small and can be minimised by making the impedance at pins 2 and 3 equal.

i.e.

$$R3 = \frac{R1 + R2}{R1 R2}$$

Any remaining offset due to the amplifier offset voltage or input current offset can be trimmed out with a zeroing potentiometer if required.

The input impedance of the closed loop amplifier is simply the value of R1.

2.2.2 Designing an Inverting Amplifier

If a relatively low gain amplifier is required, with an input voltage above about 100mV the design procedure is straightforward. Choose R1, R2 and R3 from convenient values in the come-in-handy box. As a rough rule of thumb choose R1 to be about 10k and work on from there.

For lower input voltages and higher gains, slightly more care is necessary, and the following check list should be followed.

1. V_{IO} is not particularly important since it can be nulled out, but the change in V_{IO} with temperature is often critical. Work out $\propto V_{IO}$ over the expected temperature range (when in doubt use 30°C). This should be smaller than your input signal by a factor of at least ten. If not choose a better amplifier.

2. Check that the offset due to the bias current ($I_{IB}.R1$) is less than the input signal. If not, reduce R1 or choose a better amplifier. Any small offset can be trimmed out by the zeroing potentiometer.

3. Given R1, R2 can now be calculated using the formula given. Check now for temperature variations on the offset current $\propto I_{IO}$. The equivalent offset is $\propto I_{IO}.R2$. If this is unacceptably large choose a better amplifier or reduce R1 and start again.

4. Calculate R3 as described earlier.

The above analysis assumes that R1 is fed from a low impedance source. If this is not true, R1 should be replaced by $(R1 + R_S)$ in the equations where R_S is the source resistance, or an interposing high input impedance buffer used.

2.3 NON-INVERTING AMPLIFIER

2.3.1 Description

The classic non-inverting amplifier is shown on Fig.2.2. By similar arguments to those in section 2.2 we can say that the voltages on pins 2 and 3 will be equal. By simple analysis, the voltage on pin 2 is given by:—

$$E_1 = E_{out} \cdot \frac{R1}{R1 + R2}$$

since $E_{in} = E_1$ as described above

$$E_{in} = E_{out} \cdot \frac{R1}{R1 + R2}$$

or

$$\frac{E_{out}}{E_{in}} = \frac{R1 + R2}{R1} \cdot$$

To minimise the offset due to the bias current, R3 should be chosen such that

$$R3 = \frac{R1 \cdot R2}{R1 + R2}$$

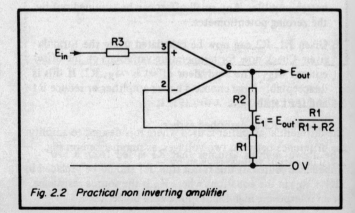

Fig. 2.2   Practical non inverting amplifier

18

The input impedance of the non inverting amplifier is very high.

2.3.2 Designing a Non-inverting Amplifier

Procedures 1 to 4 in section 2.2.2 apply to both inverting and non-inverting amplifiers.

2.4 BUFFER AMPLIFIER

A unity gain version of the non-inverting amplifier is shown in Fig.2.3. This acts as a "super" emitter follower, and has a very high input impedance. It is a very useful circuit where a buffer stage is required. In most applications the only design limitation is $\propto V_{IO}$.

The buffer amplifier is very effective when used with FET input amplifiers.

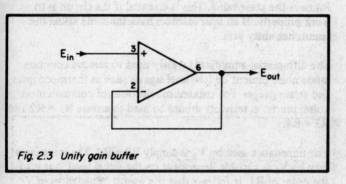

Fig. 2.3 Unity gain buffer

2.5 DIFFERENTIAL AMPLIFIER

The differential amplifier is used where it is desired to amplify the difference between two voltages, as summarised on Fig. 2.4. The output voltage is given by:—

$$E_{out} = - \frac{R_b}{R_a} (V_1 - V_2)$$

19

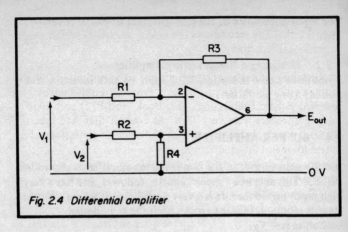

Fig. 2.4 Differential amplifier

if R1 = R2 = R_a and R3 = R4 = R_b

Note that both input resistors have the same value, and R3 and R4 have the same value. This is essential if the circuit is to work properly. If all four resistors have the same value, the circuit has unity gain.

The differential amplifier is widely used to remove common mode noise present on low level signals such as thermocouples and strain gauges. For maximum rejections of common mode noise, precision resistors should be used to ensure R1 = R2 and R3 = R4.

The impedance seen by V_2 is simply R2 + R4. The impedance seen by V_1 is variable dependent on the signal level, but is of the order of R1. It follows that the source impedances of V_1 and V_2 must be significantly lower than R1 and R2.

2.6   ANALOG COMPUTERS

2.6.1   Introduction
The history of the analog computer is, perhaps, one of the great ironies of the impact of integrated circuits. In the 1950's, computers split into two distinct types. The first was the

digital computer, using binary logic gates to perform computational tasks. The second was the analog computer which used operational amplifiers.

A digital computer's basic instructions are very limited (see the author's book "A Microprocessor Primer", published by Bernard Babani (publishing) Ltd, Book No.BP72) and these early computers were very slow. As a result they had great difficulty with problems involving the calculus operations of integration and differentiation.

An analog computer represents variables by voltages, and these can be continuously variable. It is very easy to perform calculus operations with operational amplifiers, so a model of the system under study is built. If we were building a model of a chemical plant, say, we would derive mathematical relationships for all the variables (flows, pressures, temperatures etc.). We could, for example, represent a temperature of $100 - 500°C$ by a voltage in the range $1 - 5$ volts at an amplifier output. When completed the model could be studied and used as a test bed for instrumentation etc.

Analog computers were very popular in the 1950's and 1960's, but the technology of the time was very restrictive. Valve operational amplifiers drifted in an alarming manner and transistor versions required very careful design. Nonetheless most engineering design offices and universities had an analog machine tucked away somewhere, tended by a team of engineers because these machines were BIG as well as temperamental.

The arrival of integrated circuits should have revolutionised analog computers as cheap, small, and above all stable, DC amplifiers became available. Unfortunately the same technology changed digital computers by increasing their speed to the point where complex mathematical calculations could be done in a reasonable time.

Analog computers have now almost followed the "Dodo" into the history books, which is very sad because building an analog model of a process is very instructive. The technique of analog

21

computers is still very valid, however, and the circuits described below have many applications outside computing. The adder, for example, is the basis of the audio mixer in section 4.3.

2.6.2 Adders and Subtractors

In an analog computer, variables are represented by voltages. The first requirement is an adder to sum various signals. This is achieved by Fig.2.5 which is a variation of the inverting amplifier of section 2.2.

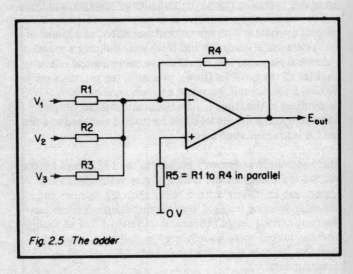

Fig. 2.5 The adder

The general relationship is:—

$$E_{out} = -\left(\frac{R4.V_1}{R1} + \frac{R4.V_2}{R2} + \frac{R4.V_3}{R3} \right)$$

If all resistors are equal we get:—

$$E_{out} = -(V_1 + V_2 + V_3).$$

Note the minus sign. Care must be taken with the signs in analog computers. If a sign inversion is required at any point a unity gain inverter can be used.

Subtraction can be achieved by either addition with one signal inverted or by use of the differential amplifier of section 2.5.

Multiplication by a constant is achieved by an inverting or non-inverting amplifier of the correct gain.

As an example, consider the simultaneous equations:—

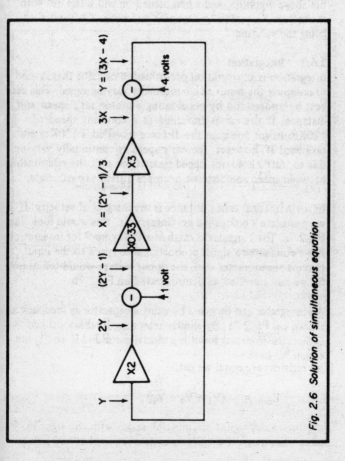

Fig. 2.6 Solution of simultaneous equation

23

$$3X - Y = 4$$
$$2Y - 3X = 1$$

where we wish to find X and Y. These can be rearranged as:—

$$Y = 3X - 4$$
$$X = (2Y-1)/3$$

Examination of the circuit of Fig.2.6 will show that it obeys the above equation, and when turned on will settle out with the voltage X equal to 3 volts and Y to 5 volts; X = 3 and Y = 5 being the solution.

2.6.3 Integration

Integration is an operation performed in calculus that is used to compute the result of a continually varying signal. This can best be understood by considering a motor car's speed and distance. If the car is travelling at a constant speed of 120Km/hr for one hour the distance travelled is 120Km, no problem! If, however, the car's speed is continually varying due to traffic hold ups, speed restrictions etc., the relationship between speed and distance becomes difficult to calculate.

In mathematical terms distance is the integral of velocity. If we postulate a box called an "integrator" this would look like Fig.2.7a. The $\int$ sign is the mathematical symbol for integration. If we connected a signal proportional to speed to the input (from a speedometer say), the ouput voltage would tell us how far we had travelled, as demonstrated on Fig.2.7b.

An integrator can be made by using a capacitor as feedback as shown on Fig.2.8a. By similar reasoning to that outlined earlier, the inverting input is a virtual earth and I_1 and I_2 are equal. We have:—

$$I_1 = \frac{V_{in}}{R1}$$

$$I_2 = \frac{dV_{out}}{dt} C$$

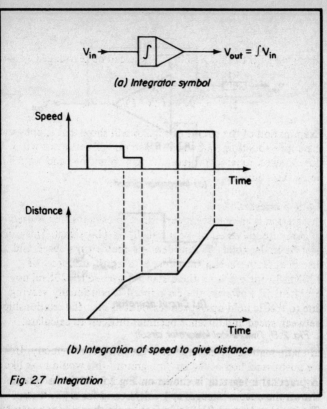

$$V_{in} \longrightarrow \boxed{\int} \longrightarrow V_{out} = \int V_{in}$$

(a) Integrator symbol

(b) Integration of speed to give distance

Fig. 2.7 Integration

Since

$$I_1 = I_2$$

$$\frac{V_{in}}{R1} = -\frac{dV_{out}C}{dt}$$

or

$$V_{out} = \frac{1}{R1C} \int V_{in} dt.$$

For readers unused to the calculus notation, this can be best understood by Fig. 2.8b. We have a step input V_{in}. The output is a ramp falling at $V_{in}/R1C$ volts per second.

25

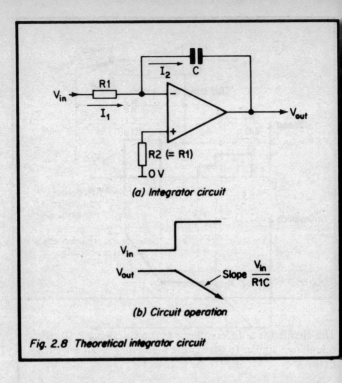

(a) Integrator circuit

Slope $\dfrac{V_{in}}{R1C}$

(b) Circuit operation

Fig. 2.8 Theoretical integrator circuit

A practical integrator is shown on Fig.2.9. With the values shown the output changes at 1 volt/second for a 1 volt step. The zeroing control RV1 is, in fact, more than a zero control since it is used to balance out the input bias current which would be integrated if left uncorrected.

RV1 should therefore be adjusted until V_{out} stabilises for zero volts in. In practice this will be impossible to achieve, and RV1 should be set for minimum drift. SW1 is therefore included to discharge C1 prior to use.

2.6.4 Differentiator

Differentiation is the calculus operation used to determine the rate of change of a varying signal. This is similar to working out the acceleration of a car from its observation of the speed.

26

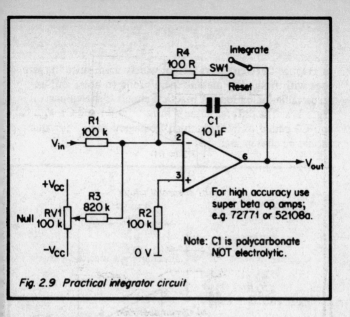

Fig. 2.9 Practical integrator circuit

The circuit for a differentiator is shown on Fig.2.10. By calculation similar to that in the preceeding section we find that.—

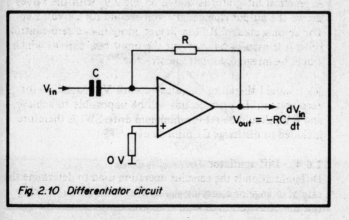

$$V_{out} = -RC\frac{dV_{in}}{dt}$$

Fig. 2.10 Differentiator circuit

27

$$V_{out} = -RC \frac{dV_{in}}{dt}.$$

In practice differentiators are not widely used, since the gain rises with frequency making them prone to noise and unpredictable oscillations. A practical circuit is shown on Fig.2.11a. The differentiator is formed by R1 and C1 with R2 and C2 added to limit the high frequency gain. The values should be chosen such that:—

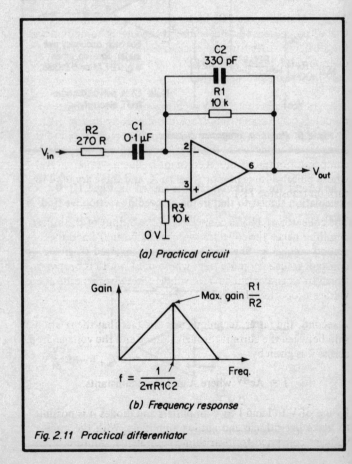

(a) Practical circuit

(b) Frequency response

Fig. 2.11 Practical differentiator

$$R1 \ C2 \ = \ R2 \ C1$$

The response is shown on Fig.2.11b, and exhibits the characteristics of a differentiator up to a frequency given by:—

$$f = \frac{1}{2\pi R1C2}$$

after which the gain falls. The maximum gain is R1/R2.

2.6.5   Multipliers and Dividers

One of the reasons for the demise of the analog computer was the difficulty of performing accurate multiplication and division. The circuits are complex, even with IC Op Amps, so only the principles will be given.

The simplest multiplier uses a pulse width and pulse height modulator, and is shown in block diagram form on Fig.2.12. The circuit starts with a sawtooth oscillator which is fed to a comparator along with the first input voltage X. The comparator output is thus a constant frequency square wave whose pulse width is proportional to X, and these are used to turn on transistor TR1.

The collector of TR1 is connected to the output of the buffer amplifier hence the collector switches between 0V and the second voltage Y. The resulting signal is inverted to give a constant frequency pulse train whose pulse width is proportional to X, and height to Y. A simple filter gives an output voltage proportional to X.Y.

A second, and faster, technique uses the fact that the relationship between the current through a diode and the voltage drop across it is given by:—

$$I = Ae^{BV} \text{ where A and B are constants.}$$

By use of V to I and I to V amplifiers and diodes it is possible to make logarithmic and antilog amplifiers. With the input voltages converted to logarithmic equivalents, multiplication

29

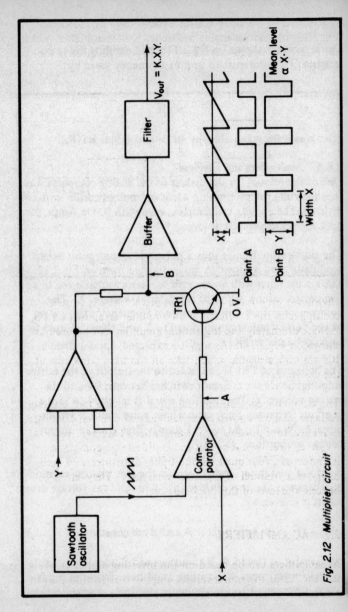

Fig. 2.12 *Multiplier circuit*

is achieved by addition and an antilog stage as shown on Fig.2.13. In practice analog multiplier ICs are available, which simplifies the design considerably! Typical of these is the CA3091.

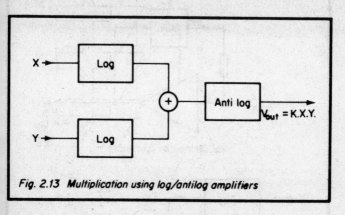

Fig. 2.13 Multiplication using log/antilog amplifiers

Division is even more complex. A simple way is to use a multiplier in the feedback of an amplifier as shown on Fig. 2.14a. Alternately the log/antilog amplifier can be used as shown on Fig.2.14b. As may be expected, special divider ICs are now available which take all the hard work out of the design.

The circuits above can only multiply or divide two positive voltages, and are known as single quadrant circuits. There are, in reality, four possible sign combinations (+ve.+ve; +ve.−ve; −ve.+ve; −ve.−ve). A circuit to handle all sign combinations is known as a four quadrant multiplier or divider, and their design is a triumph of Op Amp versatility. They are a bit beyond the level of this book however!

2.7 AC AMPLIFIERS

AC amplifiers can be based on the inverting amplifier of section 2.2 or the non-inverting amplifier of section 2.3. In general AC amplifiers are required to work on a single supply

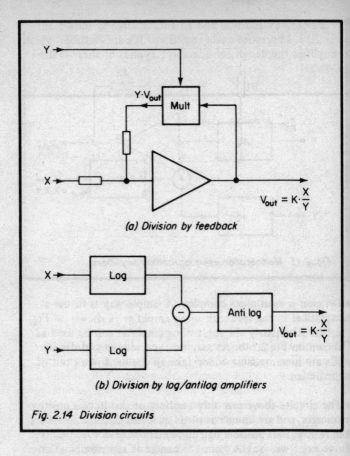

(a) Division by feedback

$$V_{out} = K \cdot \frac{X}{Y}$$

(b) Division by log/antilog amplifiers

$$V_{out} = K \cdot \frac{X}{Y}$$

Fig. 2.14 Division circuits

rail, so the circuits below are shown with a single supply which will usually be in the range 15 volts to 30 volts.

A simple inverting amplifier is shown on Fig.2.15. The circuit is biased by R1 and R2 with C2 decoupling the non-inverting input, and R4 keeping the output midway between the supply and 0V. The gain is determined by R3 and R4 as described earlier. The low frequency response is determined by C1, which should have significantly lower impedance than R3 at the lowest frequency required. The high frequency response   is

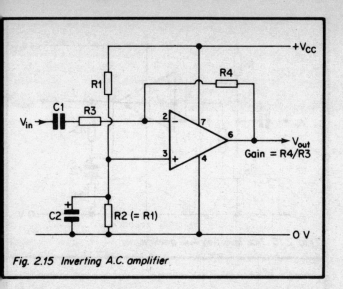

Fig. 2.15 Inverting A.C. amplifier

determined by the amplifier itself. The input impedance is simply R3.

The non-inverting amplifier is, however, usually preferred for AC amplifiers because of its high input impedance and low signal to noise ratio. A common arrangement is shown on Fig. 2.16. The circuit is biased by R1 and R2, and the gain determined by R3 and R4 as described earlier. R1 and R2 will normally be high value resistors (e.g. 470k) to maintain the high input impedance. For all practical purposes the input impedance will be the value of R1 and R2 in parallel. The low frequency response will be determined by C1 and C2, but because R1 and R2 are high valued and R4 is relatively low value the effect of C2 will be crucial in most amplifiers. C2 should be chosen such that its impedance is considerably lower than R4 at the lowest frequency required.

Where a very high input impedance is required, bootstrapping can be used as shown on Fig.2.17. The bias is set by R1 and R2 and the gain by R4 and R2 as described earlier. The non-inverting input is biased by R3, but because the signals at both

33

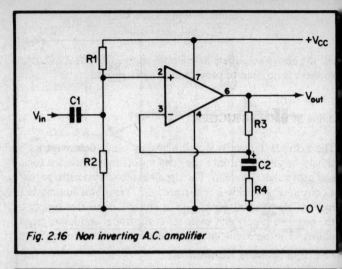

Fig. 2.16 Non inverting A.C. amplifier

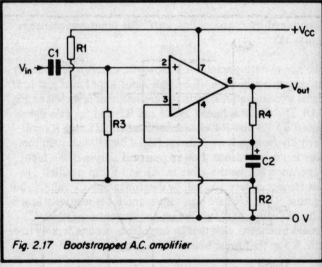

Fig. 2.17 Bootstrapped A.C. amplifier

inputs are equal in both amplitude and phase, the input impedance is very high. To a first approximation the input impedance is given by:—

$$R_{in} = \frac{\text{Amplifier Open Loop Gain}}{\text{Closed Loop Gain}} \times R3$$

All the above amplifiers have unity gain to DC offset effects, so there is no need to provide zeroing facilities.

2.8   SCHMITT TRIGGER

The Schmitt Trigger is a circuit widely used to convert a slowly varying signal into the crisp on/off signals used in logic and other digital systems. The circuit exhibits hysterisis, in that a considerable backlash is designed in. This is best summarised by Fig.2.18. The output thus is at either the positive supply or the negative supply and switches at the upper and lower trigger points. The backlash gives considerable protection against jitter on the digital output.

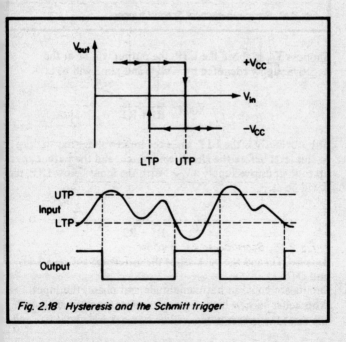

Fig. 2.18 Hysteresis and the Schmitt trigger

Schmitt triggers are available in ICs (e.g. 7414), but these have fixed trigger points. A versatile Schmitt trigger with adjustable trigger points can be made with an Op Amp and two resistors as shown on Fig.2.19.

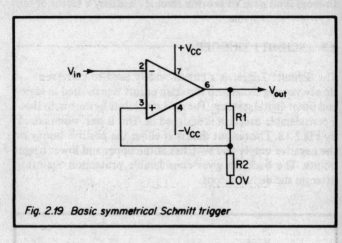

Fig. 2.19 Basic symmetrical Schmitt trigger

Suppose V_{in} is above the UTP; the output will be at the negative supply (denoted by $-V_{CC}$) and pin 3 will be at:—

$$-V_{CC} \cdot \frac{R2}{R1 + R2}$$

This obviously is the LTP, since the input voltage has to drop to this level before the circuit will switch, and the output goes up to the positive supply $+V_{CC}$. With the input below LTP, pin 3 will be at:

$$+V_{CC} \cdot \frac{R2}{R1 + R2}$$

This is UTP, and the backlash is the difference between LTP and UTP.

With equal positive and negative supplies (as will usually be the case) the trigger points will be symmetrical about 0V, and

36

the hysterisis will be twice the trigger points. If a non symmetrical response is required this can easily be provided by the circuit of Fig.2.20 where R2 is returned to a voltage of V_2 provided by the potentiometer RV1. It is important that the resistance of RV1 is lower than R1 + R2 by a factor of ten to ensure V_2 is stable.

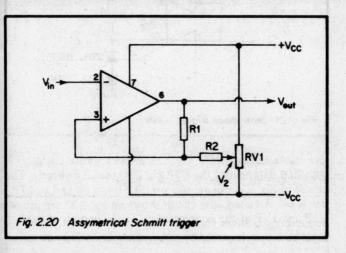

Fig. 2.20 Assymetrical Schmitt trigger

The mathematics of this circuit is slightly more complex, but the UTP is given by.—

$$\frac{R1V_2 + R2 \,(+V_{CC})}{R1 + R2}$$

and the LTP by:—

$$\frac{R1V_2 - R2 \,(-V_{CC})}{R1 + R2}.$$

Care should be taken in applying the correct polarities in the above equation.

If the supplies are not particularly stable, the trigger points may vary unacceptably. Zener diodes should then be used to

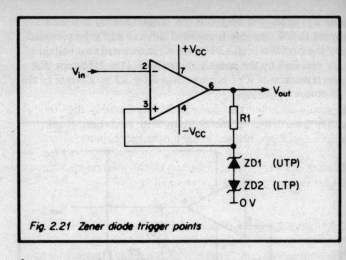

Fig. 2.21 Zener diode trigger points

give stable trigger points. Fig.2.21 shows a simple circuit,
with ZD1 determining the UTP and ZD2 the LTP directly. The
circuit of Fig.2.21 can only have a UTP above 0V and an LTP
below 0V. An alternative circuit shown on Fig.2.22 can provide
UTP and LTP of the same polarity. The operation of the

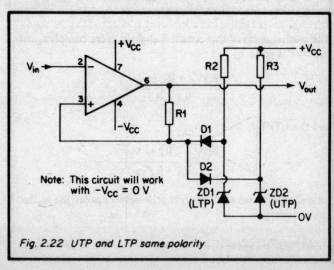

Note: This circuit will work
with −V$_{CC}$ = 0 V

Fig. 2.22 UTP and LTP same polarity

circuit is straightforward, but the Zener bias resistors R2, R3 should be considerably lower in value than R1. This is no great problem, since R1 has to supply minimal current to the non-inverting input. Obviously ZD2 determines the UTP, and ZD1 the LTP.

It should be noted that some amplifiers (notably the 709) suffer from latch up when driven into saturation. Such amplifiers cannot be used in Schmitt trigger circuits.

In section 3.3 (Function Generator) a non-inverting Schmitt trigger is described as part of an oscillator.

2.9   INCREASED CURRENT OUTPUT

Most operational amplifiers can source, or sink current up to 10mA. This is quite adequate for many applications, but quite often significantly higher currents are required. Higher current outputs can be obtained by the use of additional components.

The simplest circuit uses an NPN and a PNP transistor connected as two emitter followers as shown on Fig.2.23. For higher currents Darlington connected transistors can be used,

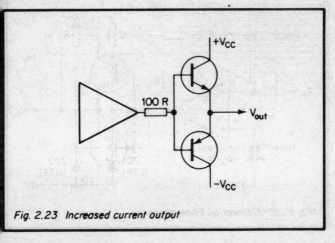

Fig. 2.23 Increased current output

either by means of four discrete transistors or with two Darlington ICs such as the TIP121 (NPN) or TIP126 (PNP). It should be noted that the use of booster transistors will reduce the available output range by about 1 volt in each direction (about 1.5 volts for Darlingtons).

If booster transistors are used, it is very important to take the feedback from the junction of the two emitters as shown on Fig.2.24. This will ensure correct circuit operation. Taking the feedback from the Op Amp output results in some very odd effects!

Variations on the circuit of Fig.2.23 will be found later in the Audio section, where they make useful and simple audio amplifiers.

The choice of transistors is determined mainly by the current gain. The Op Amp can source or sink 10mA, hence if the transistors in Fig.2.23 have a β of 20 (a reasonable figure for a power transistor) we could drive a 200mA load. With Darlingtons a β of 1000 is easily obtained, so we could, in theory, drive a 10 Amp load, although this would be

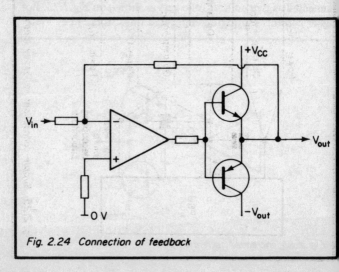

Fig. 2.24 Connection of feedback

impractical for other reasons! The output transistors will dissipate a fair amount of heat, the maximum dissipation occurring when the output is halfway between 0V and a supply rail. For example, if we are driving 500mA from a ±15V supply, the maximum dissipation in the output transistors will occur when the output voltage is 7.5V. The current will be 250mA,

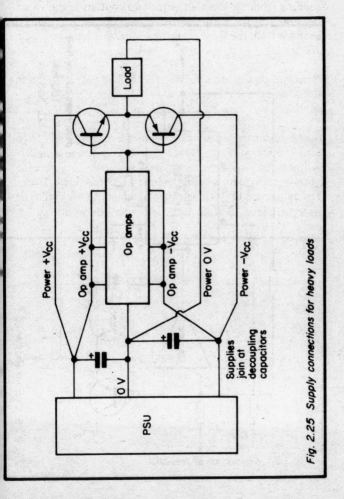

Fig. 2.25 Supply connections for heavy loads

giving a dissipation of nearly 2 watts. In most cases heat sinks of some sort will be necessary.

If high currents are used, care should be taken to use sensible return wires, as shown on Fig.2.25. Do not take several amps down Vero Board tracks! In extreme cases, separate power and Op Amp supplies can be used.

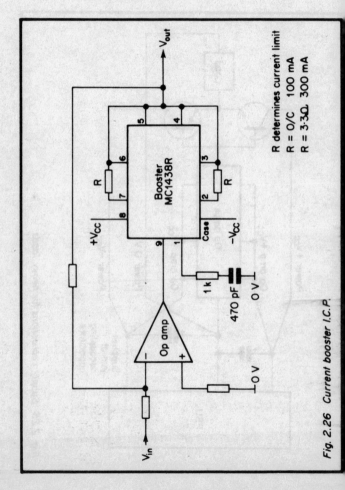

Fig. 2.26 Current booster I.C.P.

Where moderate currents are needed (up to 300mA) an elegant, although slightly expensive, solution is to use the current booster IC available from several manufacturers (MC1438R). This is connected as Fig.2.26 and gives increased current output for little trouble. The earlier comments regarding feedback still apply and feedback should still be taken from the load side of the booster IC.

2.10   POSITIVE/NEGATIVE AMPLIFIER

The circuit in Fig.2.27 is an ingenious combination of an inverting amplifier and a non-inverting amplifier. With the contact closed, the amplifier is identical to the inverting amplifier of section 2.2 with unity gain.

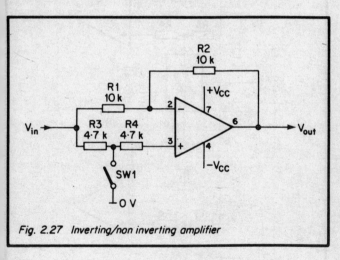

Fig. 2.27   Inverting/non inverting amplifier

With the contact open, the amplifier effectively becomes a voltage follower and is now a non-inverting amplifier with unity gain.

The contact in Fig.2.27 can be a simple relay contact or switch, but electronic contacts can also be used. In Fig.2.28a an FET is used. With the gate positive the FET exhibits a low

43

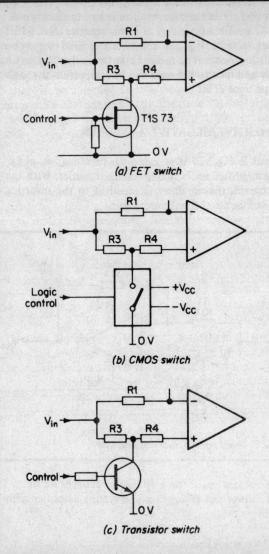

Fig. 2.28 Switches for inverting/non inverting amplifier

resistance between source and drain, taking the junction of R3, R4 to 0V. With the gate negative below the pinch off voltage the FET is turned off. It is important to use an FET with a low value of $R_{DS(on)}$. An alternative FET switch is the CMOS analog switches such as the 4016 or the 7502, the latter being simpler to use with its ±15V supplies and 0 to +10V gate signal. Fig. 2.28b shows a 7502 being driven from a CMOS logic circuit. Both the 4016 and the 7502 are quad devices, so the switching circuit above leaves 3 unused gates in the device.

If the input voltage is of constant polarity, a transistor can be used as the contact. In Fig.2.28c a simple 2N3704 (or other GP transistor) is turned on to connect the junction of R3, R4 to 0V. The transistor does introduce a small offset of about 0.2V in the inverting mode, but this is normally acceptable with an input range of 0 to 15 volts.

Almost any Op Amp can be used in this circuit, the only care that is needed is in ensuring that the input bias currents do not cause unacceptable offsets. The values shown will suit most common Op Amps.

The circuit finds many applications in industrial control, where it is used to invert the output from a unipolar digital to analogue converter (DAC). The circuit is also useful in driving indicators from a bipolar signal, with the electronic switch driven from a polarity detector. In section 3.4 the circuit is used as the basis of a voltage controlled oscillator.

CHAPTER 3
OSCILLATORS

3.1   INTRODUCTION

Oscillators can be made using discrete components and digital ICs, but Op Amps allow oscillators to be made easily when large amplitude outputs or odd waveforms are required. This section describes several useful oscillator circuits using operational amplifiers.

3.2   SCHMITT TRIGGER OSCILLATOR

Any inverting Schmitt Trigger can be turned into an oscillator by connecting a resistor from output to input and a capacitor from input to 0V as Fig.3.1. The input will rise and fall expo-nentionally between the UTP and the LTP, and the output will switch between the two output levels. The period is thus determined by the supply rails, the values of R and C and UTP and LTP.

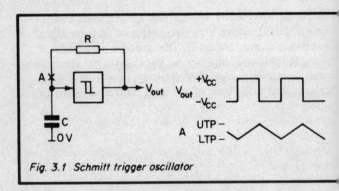

Fig. 3.1 Schmitt trigger oscillator

A practical circuit is shown on Fig.3.2. This is simply the Schmitt Trigger of section 2.8 with the additional timing resistor and capacitor. The calculation of the period is somewhat involved, and can be simplified by always keeping the

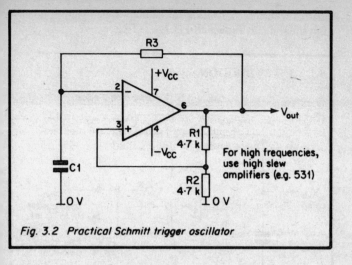

Fig. 3.2 Practical Schmitt trigger oscillator

values of R1,R2 as shown. With these values, the period is
determined by R and C as below.

$$T = 2.2 \times C1 \times R3 \text{ secs}$$

$$\text{freq} = \frac{1}{2.2 \times C1 \times R3} \quad \text{Hz}$$

The circuit has two possible outputs. On the Op Amp output
we have a square wave with amplitude equal to the difference
between the supply rails, and an exponential waveform on the
inverting input of amplitude about 75% of the difference
between the supply rails.

Altering the value of R or C will alter the period, leaving the
amplitude of the exponential output unchanged but altering
the slope.

Altering the value of R1 or R2 will alter the period and the
amplitude of the exponential output, leaving the slope
unchanged. It follows that a very versatile oscillator can be
made by making R a variable resistor and R1 and R2 variable

resistors with the connection to the non-inverting input taken from the slider as shown on Fig.3.3.

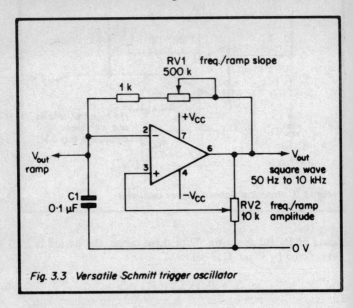

Fig. 3.3 Versatile Schmitt trigger oscillator

With the addition of two diodes as shown on Fig.3.4 the mark/space ratio of the oscillator can be varied. Since C charges via D1 and R_a and discharges via D2 and R_b the mark/space can be varied without greatly affecting the period.

The Schmitt trigger oscillator will work up to frequencies in excess of 50kHz if Op Amps such as the 748 are used. It should be noted that some amplifiers (notably the 709) suffer from latch up when driven into saturation. Such amplifiers cannot be used for either the Schmitt trigger or the Schmitt trigger oscillator.

3.3   FUNCTION GENERATOR

The circuit in the preceeding section is a useful oscillator, but only produces an exponential output. With an additional

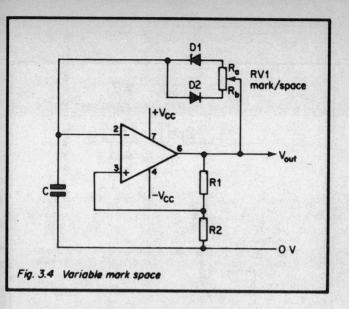

Fig. 3.4 Variable mark space

amplifier a true ramp output can be obtained.

The circuit is shown on Fig.3.5. IC1 is a Schmitt trigger, with the signal input being applied to the non-inverting input by R3. This connection differs from the Schmitt trigger of section 2.8 in that it produces a non-inverting circuit which is necessary to make the circuit oscillate.

The output of IC1 is at either supply rail, depending on the voltage at IC2 output. IC2 is connected as an integrator with rate of rise determined by R2, RV2 and C1. The output of IC2 thus ramps up and down between the trigger points of IC1.

RV1 and RV2 both adjust the frequency of oscillation. RV1 adjusts the amplitude but leaves the slope unchanged. RV2 adjusts the slope leaving the amplitude unchanged. The two adjustments thus give considerable control over the output waveform. By the addition of two diodes and RV3 as shown on Fig.3.5b the rising and falling slopes can be independently adjusted.

49

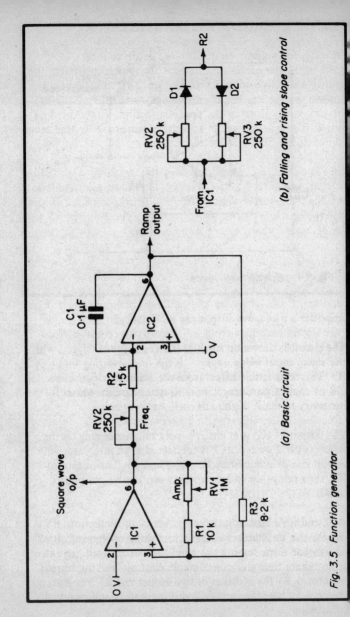

(b) Falling and rising slope control

(a) Basic circuit

Fig. 3.5 Function generator

50

3.4   VOLTAGE CONTROLLED OSCILLATOR

An elegant voltage controlled oscillator can be made combining the oscillator from the previous section with the positive/negative amplifier of section 2.10. The circuit is shown on Fig.3.6. IC2 is an integrator and IC3 a Schmitt trigger as described in the previous section. The upper and lower trigger points of the Schmitt trigger are set by the zener diodes ZD1, ZD2. (see section 2.8).

IC1 is connected as a positive/negative amplifier with the control voltage applied as an input, and the sign determined by the field effect transistor FET1. The output of IC3 controls FET1, hence the output of IC1 will be either $+V_{in}$, or $-V_{in}$ as determined by the output signal.

The output of IC1 is applied to the integrator IC2. The circuit thus forms an oscillator similar to section 3.3. The larger the input voltage, the faster will the output of IC2 rise or fall, and hence the frequency of oscillation will increase. The relationship between frequency and input voltage is, in fact, very linear and the circuit will operate over a range from 50Hz to 10kHz with the values shown.

If the circuit is to be operated with values of V_{in} below 50mV, the input voltage offset should be balanced out by the addition of RV1. If the circuit is to be operated at high frequencies, amplifiers with high slew rates should be used for IC1 and IC3.

3.5   WIEN BRIDGE OSCILLATORS

3.5.1   Introduction
Sine Wave Oscillators with any reasonable degree of purity are rather difficult to make. For oscillation to occur, the total phase shift round the amplifier must be 360 degrees and the gain exactly unity. The first criteria is not difficult to achieve, but the second is usually achieved by allowing

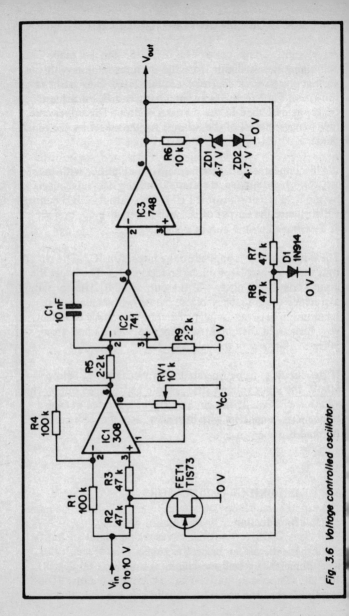

Fig. 3.6 Voltage controlled oscillator

some part of the amplifier to saturate with corresponding waveform distortion.

The sine wave oscillators in this (and succeeding) sections use various methods to control the total closed loop gain and avoid waveform distortion with varying degrees of success.

The two oscillators following are based on the Wien bridge of Fig.3.7. This circuit has the property that V_{in} and V_{out} are in phase at one specific frequency. If it is used as a positive feedback network round an amplifier, oscillation will occur at the specific frequency.

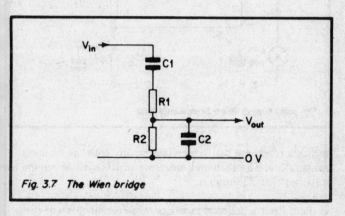

Fig. 3.7 The Wien bridge

To simplify calculations, R1 = R2 = R, and C1 = C2 = C. The frequency is then given by:—

$$f = \frac{1}{2\pi RC} \quad Hz$$

If a variable frequency is required R1 and R2 should be made variable by a dual track linear potentiometer.

3.5.2 Practical Wien Bridge Oscillator

The simplest Wien Bridge oscillator is shown on Fig.3.8. R1, R2, C1, C2 provide the feedback as described above. The amplitude is stabilised by the bulb LP1. A lamp bulb has, by

53

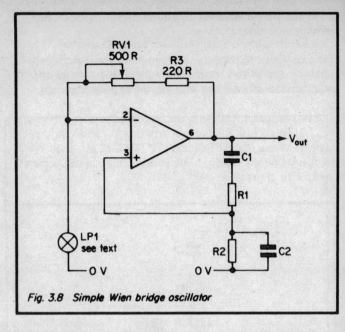

Fig. 3.8 Simple Wien bridge oscillator

design, a resistance which increases rapidly with the filament temperature. The bulb and resistance of RV1/R3 determine the amplifier closed loop gain.

If the output amplitude increases, the current through the bulb will increase, causing the bulb resistance to increase as it gets hotter. This in turn reduces the amplifier gain and the output amplitude.

The circuit thus oscillates at a frequency determined by the feedback network, and amplitude determined by RV1. The lack of amplifier saturation assures a clean output waveform, although the thermal time constant of LP1 means the circuit can take several seconds to stabilise.

The circuit will operate on any supply from ±6V to ±15V, but the supply should be regulated. LP1 should be chosen to have a nominal voltage about 1.5 times the rail voltage and a nominal current of around 40mA.

3.5.3 Amplitude Stabilised Wien Bridge Oscillator
The oscillator in the previous section used a lamp bulb to stabilise the output level. A more elegant circuit, shown on Fig.3.9, uses an FET to achieve the same purpose.

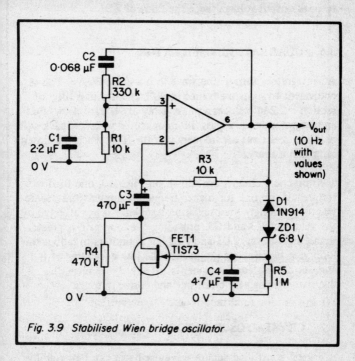

Fig. 3.9 Stabilised Wien bridge oscillator

The Wien Bridge comprises R1, R2, C1, C2 as before. For best results R2 should be about 30 x R1, and C1 about 30 x C2. The full equation is then:—

$$f = \frac{1}{2\pi\sqrt{(R1 \times R2 \times C1 \times C2)}} Hz$$

The amplifier gain is determined by R3 and R4 in parallel with the on resistance of FET1. For negative peaks smaller than the value of ZD1, C4 will be discharged by R5, and FET1 will present a low resistance between source and drain. If the output amplitude exceeds the value of ZD1, C4 will charge negatively, and FET1 will increase the resistance between source and drain. This in turn reduces the amplifier gain and the output amplitude. The circuit thus stabilises with the peak to peak output voltage twice the value of ZD1.

3.6 QUADRATURE OSCILLATOR

All integrators turn a sine wave into a cosine wave. This is equivalent to a phase advance of 90°. The low pass filter of section 5.2.2 introduces a phase delay of 90°. It follows that an integrator and low pass filter connected with feedback will oscillate at the cut off frequency of the filter when the closed loop gain is unity.

Two practical circuits are shown on Fig.3.10, one for low frequency and one for higher frequency applications. Somewhat interestingly the oscillation frequency is not affected by the values of R3 and C3, providing the loop gain is greater than unity. Zeners ZD1 and ZD2 act as limiters to reduce the loop gain by clipping the peaks. The low pass filter of IC1 and its associated components effectively remove the distortion giving very clean sine and cosine outputs.

3.7 CRYSTAL OSCILLATOR

A crystal controlled square wave oscillator can be made by using a crystal in the shunt resonant mode and an amplifier. The circuit is shown on Fig.3.11. The circuit oscillates at the frequency where the crystal exhibits minimum impedance. The crystal thus works at its fundamental frequency. It should be noted that most RF crystals nominally operate at some overtone frequency and will operate at some fraction of their marked frequency in this circuit.

The amplifier must have high frequency gain and high slew

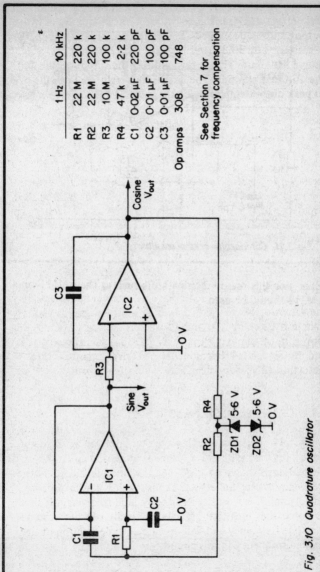

	1 Hz	10 kHz
R1	22 M	220 k
R2	22 M	220 k
R3	10 M	100 k
R4	47 k	2·2 k
C1	0·02 μF	220 pF
C2	0·01 μF	100 pF
C3	0·01 μF	100 pF
Op amps	308	748

See Section 7 for
frequency compensation

Fig. 3.10 Quadrature oscillator

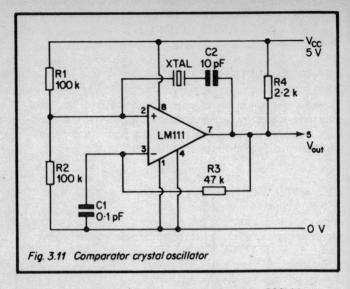

Fig. 3.11 Comparator crystal oscillator

rates. For this reason, comparators such as the LM111 or LM311 should be used.

CHAPTER 4
AUDIO CIRCUITS

4.1 INTRODUCTION

The ease with which the response of an operational amplifier can be controlled by feedback makes it very suitable as the basis for audio circuits. This section describes many varied applications using Op Amps in audio.

4.2 FIELD TELEPHONES

A simple communication link is required for many events; sports days, car rallies, industrial commissioning, etc. The circuit described in this section is a cheap versatile telephone link. Unlike the more common baby alarm circuit both ends can speak without a press to talk button.

The basic circuit is shown on Fig.4.1. Each end has a microphone, speaker and amplifier connected onto a 2 core cable via a series resistor. Both speakers are connected onto the line, so when either microphone is used, both speakers respond. You thus hear yourself in your own earpiece as happens with a domestic telephone. The series resistors prevent the amplifier outputs loading each other down.

The detailed circuit of one end is shown on Fig.4.2, both ends being identical. The microphone and speaker are in a normal GPO handset available from any surplus store. Resistor R1 provides bias current for the carbon microphone. IC1 is connected as a normal inverting amplifier with gain determined by R4 and R5. R6 is the series resistor connecting the amplifier output to the line. The speaker volume is determined by VR1.

It is useful to have a call facility on a pair of field telephones. This is provided by C3 which turns IC1 into an oscillator when the call PB is pressed. Note that because the speaker is

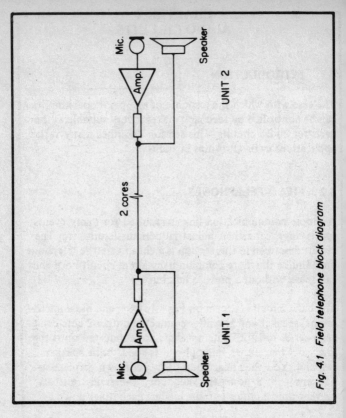

Fig. 4.1 Field telephone block diagram

connected direct to the line, the call button will alert the other unit even if it is turned off.

The author is involved in commissioning industrial control equipment, and has been using a pair of these phones for some time. They have proved invaluable and work reliably over cables several kilometres in length.

4.3 AUDIO MIXER

Audio mixers are used to mix several signal sources. They are

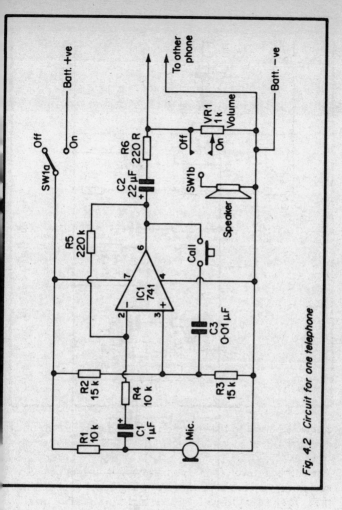

Fig. 4.2 Circuit for one telephone

therefore essential for applications like disco suites where several record and cassette decks are mixed into one power amplifier along with the DJ's voice over.

The circuit is shown on Fig.4.3. Four input sources are shown, but any reasonable number could be used. IC1 is connected

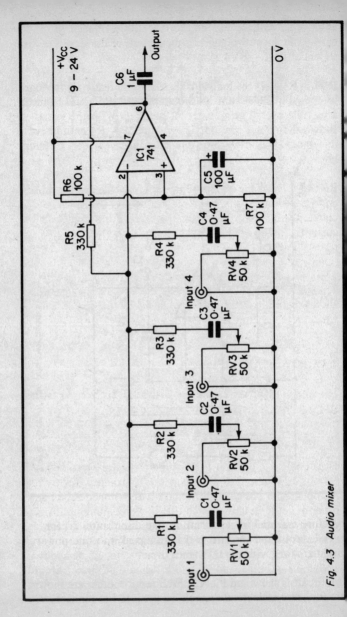

Fig. 4.3 Audio mixer

62

as an adder with the junction of R1 — R4 forming a virtual earth. The output voltage is thus the sum of the signals at the sliders of RV1 — RV4.

RV1 — RV4 set the individual levels. For a really professional looking unit slider controls should be used. R5 could be made a variable overall gain control if required. With the values shown the circuit has unity gain, but R1 — R4 could have different values if the three input signals have widely different levels.

R6 and R7 bias the circuit midway between the supply rails, and C5 decouples any noise on the supply. C1 to C4 AC couple the input signals to the input resistors, and prevent DC current flowing through the wipers on the input potentiometers.

The 741 and 709 are rather noisy devices, and should be avoided if the mixing is done with low level signals. Special audio operational amplifiers are available at slight expense which have very low noise levels, (e.g. 748).

4.4   POWER AMPLIFIER

The design of power amplifiers is a rather specialised art if Hi-Fi quality is required, but a simple power amplifier of reasonable quality can be made from an Op Amp and a few additional components.

The circuit is shown on Fig.4.4 and is basically the high current stage described in section 2.9, re-arranged slightly for AC operation. The gain of the stage is determined by R1 and R2 and should be chosen such that the maximum input signal gives an output signal just inside the supply rails. If, for example, the input signal is 0.5 volts peak to peak, and we have a 24 volt supply rail, the maximum gain will be about 20/0.5. i.e. 40 times and R1 and R2 should be chosen accordingly, 10k for R1 and 390k for R2 being suitable values. It should be remembered that the input signal peak to peak value

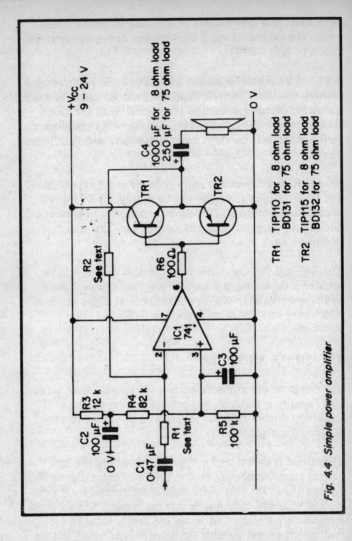

Fig. 4.4 Simple power amplifier

should be used, not the RMS value. It is useful to remember that.—

$$V_{PK \text{ to } PK} = 2 \times \sqrt{2} \times V_{RMS} \text{ (roughly 3 } \times V_{RMS})$$

Note that R2 is taken from the junction of the emitters of TR1 and TR2 to reduce the effect of the V_{BE} drops. TR1 and TR2 should be mounted on suitable heatsinks.

The maximum output power will depend on the supply voltage and the loudspeaker impedance. With a 24 volt supply and an 8 ohm speaker the maximum output power is about 6 watts. The comments in section 2.9 concerning power supply wiring should be followed implicitly to avoid interaction between input signals and supply noise. In extreme cases, the amplifier can turn into an oscillator! In addition the supply will be asked for several hundred milliamps on loud passages, and should be designed for 1 Amp rating with adequate smoothing capacitors.

4.5   AUDIO PRE-AMPLIFIER

An audio amplifier usually consists of two stages; a pre-amplifier and a power amplifier. The inputs to an amplifier come from a wide range of sources; tape decks, record player cartridges, radio tuners etc. These have different voltage amplitudes and different characteristics. A pre-amplifier is used to give a signal of constant characteristics regardless of source. This standardized signal can then be amplified further by the power amplifier.

Common signal sources are:—
a. Magnetic Cartridges used in high quality record decks. These give a low output signal of around 2mV amplitude to RIAA standard. The RIAA replay curve and its origin is too complex to discuss here, but it is sufficient to note that a magnetic cartridge requires equalisation in the pre-amplifier to give a flat response at the power amplifier input.
b. High quality Ceramic Cartridges. These have an output of around 25mV and an essentially flat response. They do, however, have the disadvantage of a very high source impedance.
c. High Output Ceramic Cartridges. These are used in lower

priced record decks, and give acceptable, but not high fidelity signals. The output from these cartridges is a high impedance signal of around 250mV amplitude.

d. Radio Tuner. Almost all tuners give an output with a flat response and an amplitude of about 100mV.

e. Tape Decks. Although the output from a tape head requires considerable equalisation, this is normally done within the tape deck itself. The signal from a tape deck is therefore similar to that from a tuner with flat response and 100mV amplitude.

A pre-amplifier thus has to deal with a wide range of signal sources of greatly different characteristics. The use of negative feedback with an operational amplifier allows a simple solution to the problem.

A useful pre-amplifier circuit is shown on Fig.4.5. The heart of the circuit is 748 amplifier IC1. The 748 is used in preference to the 741 because of its better frequency response and lower noise. For experimental purposes a 741 would suffice, however.

The amplifier is connected in its non-inverting mode (which gives lower noise, see section 2.7) with R5, R6 and R7 biasing the amplifier for unity DC gain. Offset effects are therefore negligible. Capacitor C2, however, acts as a low impedance to AC signals so the amplifier gain without the feedback via SW1b would be very high.

The circuit as drawn has 5 input sources for demonstration purposes. In practice the user would build the circuit with fewer inputs relevant to his own equipment. The coupled switches SW1a and SW1b select the source and feedback necessary to give the correct gain and response.

The tuner and tape inputs are simplest, so these will be dealt with first. These are selected on switch positions 4 and 5. The response is flat, so SW1b selects R11 as feedback. The gain is determined by the ratio of R11 and R6, C2 appearing as a low impedance to audio frequencies. With the value shown the gain is about 2 times.

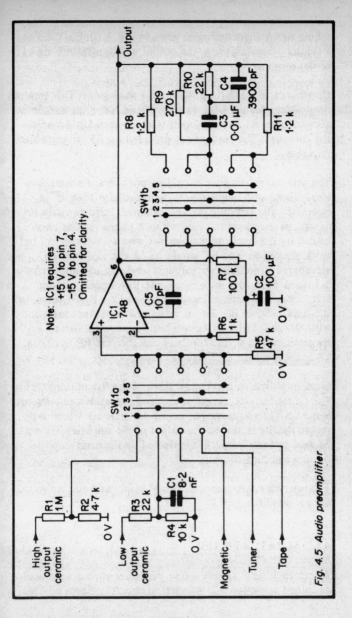

Fig. 4.5 Audio preamplifier

The magnetic cartridge is selected on switch position 3. The falling RIAA characteristic is given by R9, R10, C3, C4. For a typical 2.5mV cartridge the output will be a 200mV signal of flat response.

Ceramic cartridges have a high source impedance. This presents no problem for the high output models, since the simple attenuator of R1 and R2 provides a high impedance load to the cartridge. The feedback is provided by R8, giving a flat response.

The low output ceramic cartridges provide a problem, however. These also require a high impedance load if an essentially flat response is to be obtained. Unfortunately R5 cannot be increased in value without increasing the noise caused by the amplifier bias current, and a simple divider network similar to R1, R2 would cause the signal to be attenuated to an unacceptably low level. If a ceramic cartridge is loaded by a low impedance, the low frequencies are attenuated in a manner approximating to the RIAA curve. In the circuit shown R3, R4 provide a low impedance load, and with C1 added the characteristics are very similar to a magnetic cartridge. The feedback can then use R9, R10, C3, C4 as the magnetic cartridge did above.

Most amplifiers will only need three of the five options on Fig. 4.5. (A tape source, record source and tuner). If a single source is used SW1a and b can, of course be omitted. Where tape record facility is needed the output of the amplifier IC1 can be used since its output is unaffected by the main amplifier volume and tone controls.

The following three sections detail useful "add-ons" to go with the pre-amplifier.

4.6   SCRATCH FILTER

A scratch filter is simply a low pass filter similar to those described in section 5.2. A practical circuit is shown on Fig.

4.6. With the values shown, the circuit rejects frequencies above 5kHz. This effectively removes the hiss, crackle and pop on maltreated records without unduly affecting the actual reproduction.

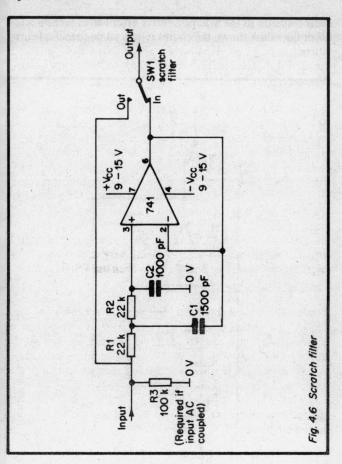

Fig. 4.6 Scratch filter

4.7 RUMBLE FILTER

Cheaper record player decks usually have a direct drive to the

69

turntable. Compared with the belt drive used on Hi-Fi decks, direct drive can cause the motor rumble to be coupled into the arm. This rumble can be removed to a large extent by the use of a filter similar to Fig.4.7.

This is similar to the high pass filters described in section 5.3. With the values shown the circuit rejects all frequencies below 50Hz.

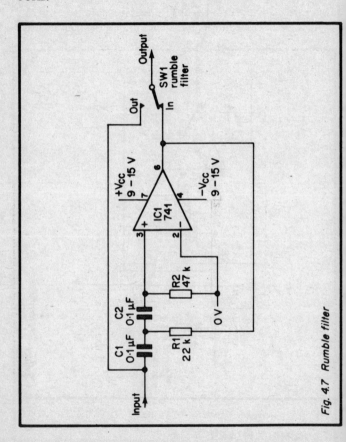

Fig. 4.7 Rumble filter

4.8 TONE CONTROL

Negative feedback allows the gain of an amplifier to be defined precisely. It follows that a very effective tone control, with separate treble and bass adjustment, can be made by using frequency dependant networks in the feedback of an amplifier.

There are many possible circuits (in fact it would be possible to fill a book with tone controls!) but one of the commonest

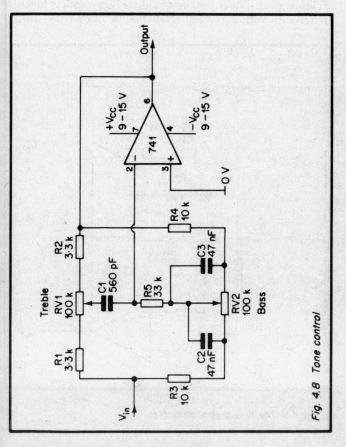

Fig. 4.8 Tone control

circuits is shown on Fig.4.8. The circuit is based on an inverting amplifier for ease of design. Although a non-inverting circuit gives lower noise (see section 2.7), tone controls are usually used after a pre-amplifier where the signal levels are quite high and the amplifier noise negligible.

At first sight the circuit of Fig.4.8 is rather forbidding, but in fact it is the combination of the two simple circuits of Fig.4.9a and b. In Fig.4.9a, RV1 is the treble control. This is a simple inverting amplifier with gain determined by RV1. The inclusion of C1 causes the circuit to have higher gain at high frequencies. With the values shown, the circuit becomes effec-

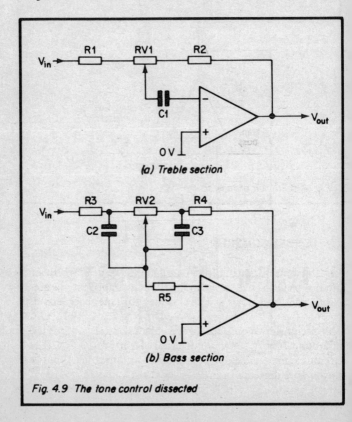

(a) Treble section

(b) Bass section

Fig. 4.9 The tone control dissected

72

tive at frequencies above 1 kHz.

Fig. 4.9b shows the bass control RV2 and the associated components. This is similar to the treble control, being a simple amplifier with gain determined by RV2. The inclusion of C2, and C3 however causes high frequencies to bypass RV2, so the bass control is only effective at low frequencies. With the values shown, RV2 becomes operational below 1kHz.

The two circuits in Fig. 4.9a and b are combined to give the tone control of Fig.4.8. The junction of C1 and R5 is a summing junction giving the combined response of Fig.4.10.

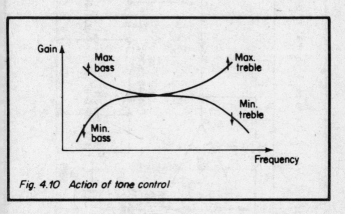

Fig. 4.10 Action of tone control

4.9   LEVEL COMPRESSOR

Level compressors are automatic gain controls used where an input signal can cover a wide range. Obvious applications are public address systems and level setting for tape recorders.

The circuit shown on Fig.4.11 will give a constant output level of around 200mV for an input signal of 2mV to 200mV. The circuit responds quickly to an increase in input level, but slowly to a decrease in input level. This is known as fast attack, slow decay, and is the normal requirement for any AGC system.

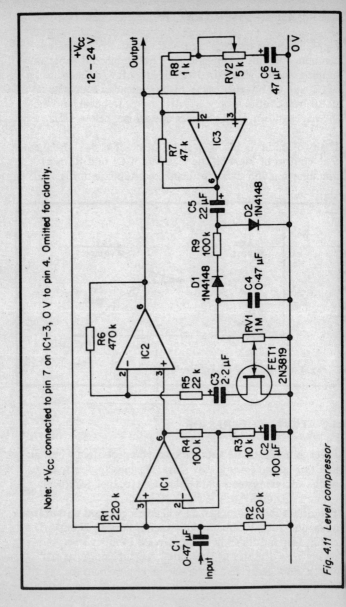

Note: +V$_{CC}$ connected to pin 7 on IC1–3, 0 V to pin 4. Omitted for clarity.

Fig. 4.11 Level compressor

74

The input signal is AC coupled by C1 to IC1 which is a conventional AC amplifier with a gain of 10. The output of IC1 is connected to IC2, another AC amplifier. The gain of IC2 is determined by R6, R5 and the value of drain-source resistance of FET1. The higher the resistance exhibited by the FET, the lower will be the gain. As we shall shortly see, the gate voltage is controlled by the signal level.

The output voltage is monitored by IC3 with gain determined by RV2. The output of IC3 is AC coupled by C5 and DC restored by D2 to give a signal at R9 that is symmetrical about 0V. This is rectified by D1 and C4 and applied to the gate of FET1. If the output level rises, the drain-source resistance of FET1 will increase as the gate goes more negative and the gain of IC2 will fall compensating for the change in signal level.

If the output level falls, C4 will discharge via RV1, decreasing the drain source resistance and increasing the gain of IC2. The output level thus remains constant for changes in the input signal. The attack time is determined by R9, C4 and the decay time by RV1, C4. RV1 and RV2 set the output level at which the circuit stabilises.

The circuit of Fig.4.11 is ideal for the experimenter, but AGC ICs can be used to simplify the design. A typical chip is the 76020 shown on Fig.4.12. This works in a similar manner to Fig.4.11. If the output voltage peaks exceed the voltage at the junction of R1, RV1, R2 capacitor C4 charges via D1 and R3 A positive voltage on C4 attenuates the input signal, reducing the output level. The 76020 has the attack/decay times set internally.

4.10   BABY ALARM

A baby alarm is an essential for any family with young children. The unit consists of a small microphone unit connected to a master amplifier by a two core cable. The master amplifier can thus listen to the nursery where the microphone is placed. A talkback facility is also included to allow the

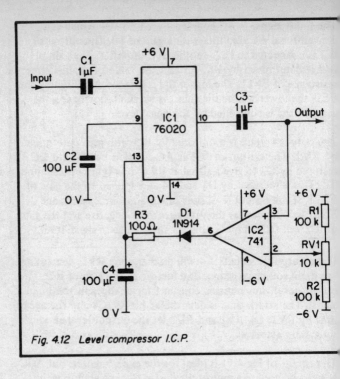

Fig. 4.12   Level compressor I.C.P.

master amplifier to speak to the remote unit. Baby alarms are available ready built, but the unit described below can be buil◄ for a fraction of the cost of a conventional baby alarm. The most expensive part of the circuit will be the cases!

The basis of the circuit is shown on Fig.4.13. We have an audi◄ amplifier, denoted by AMP, and a loudspeaker in the master unit with the press to talk switch PB1. At the remote station we simply have a microphone. It is an interesting fact that a moving coil microphone and a loudspeaker have basically the same construction. The small loudspeakers fitted in cheap transistor radios can be used both as a loudspeaker (for which they were designed) and a cheap microphone. In the circuit of◄ Fig.4.13, LS1 and LS2 are cheap loudspeakers used as both microphone and loudspeaker for economy.

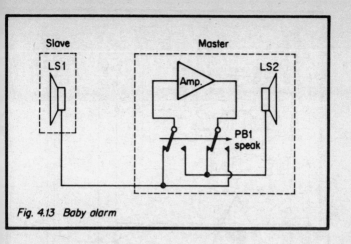

Fig. 4.13 Baby alarm

With PB1 in the normal position, LS1 acts as a microphone
connected to the amplifier input, and LS2 as a loudspeaker
connected to the amplifier output. Speech is thus conveyed
from the remote station to the master station. If PB1 is
pressed, LS1 is connected to the output, and LS2 to the
input. Speech now passes from LS2 (acting as a microphone)
to LS1 (acting as a loudspeaker).

The amplifier circuit itself is shown on Fig.4.14. This is a conventional audio amplifier using the techniques described in
section 2.7 and 2.9. IC1 is connected in the non-inverting
mode to reduce the amplifier noise. VR1 sets the gain of IC1
and acts as a volume control. IC2 is an inverting amplifier
with fixed gain. TR1 and TR2 give current gain to drive the
low impedance loads of LS1 and LS2.

The circuit runs on a single 9V battery contained in the master
unit. The current consumption is minimal in the quiescent
state, but rises when sound is being passed. Battery life thus
depends on use, but will typically be several hours on a PP3
battery. A simple mains supply unit could be used if required,
similar to those described in section 8.1.

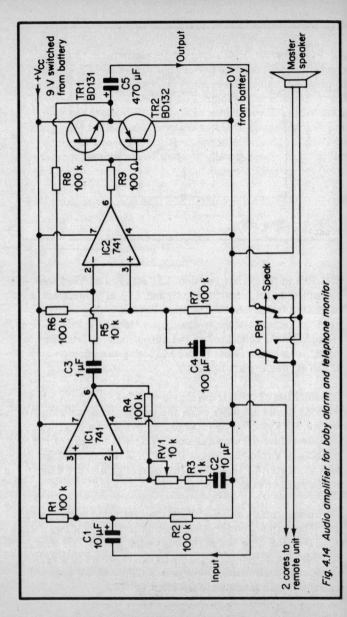

Fig. 4.14 Audio amplifier for baby alarm and telephone monitor

78

4.11 TELEPHONE MONITOR

A telephone monitor allows many people to listen to a telephone conversation. Post Office regulations forbid connection
to telephone cables, but inductive pickup units are available
from electronic hobbyshops. These consist of a multiturn coil
attached to a rubber sucker. These can be stuck to the phone
and pick up speech by electromagnetic induction. The best
position for the sticker seems to vary from phone to phone,
but the best place is usually adjacent to the handset speaker
or on the side of the phone base.

The inductive sucker is connected to the input of the amplifier
of Fig.4.14, from the previous section with a cheap loudspeaker connected to the amplifier output. In use, care must
be taken in the setting of the volume control and the
positioning of the unit to prevent the telephone microphone
picking up the amplified speech. If this occurs a banshee wail
comes from both the phone and monitor!

4.12 NOISE GENERATOR

Noise is something that designers of audio circuits normally
try to avoid. A noise generator is, however, needed as the
basis of many sound effects (steam engines, whistles, wind and
rain etc.). The circuit shown on Fig.4.15 is a simple, but effective, noise generator.

The noise is generated by TR1. The base emitter junctions of a
transistor acts as a zener diode when back biased above 5 volts.
If the biasing current is very low, the resulting zener voltage
is very noisy.

The noise from TR1 is AC coupled to IC1 connected as a high
gain amplifier giving noise of about 2 volts amplitude at the
amplifier output.

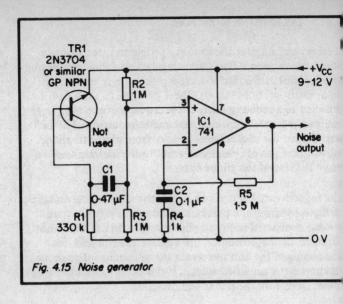

Fig. 4.15 Noise generator

CHAPTER 5
FILTERS

5.1 INTRODUCTION

Filters are required in many applications, and are often implemented by passive capacitor and inductive networks. Inductors are, however, bulky, expensive and somewhat difficult to obtain. The use of operational amplifiers with frequency selective feedback allows filters to be designed using only resistors and capacitors.

Unfortunately the design of filters can be a very technical subject involving advanced mathematical techniques such as Laplace transforms and Transfer functions. The description of filters below is therefore considerably simplified and the circuits are given as "building blocks" with minimal mathematics. Readers requiring more details should refer to any standard electronics text book for more complex analysis.

5.2 LOW PASS FILTER

5.2.1 Simple Low Pass Filter
The simplest possible low pass filter is shown on Fig.5.1. The capacitor C has infinite impedance at DC, and the low frequency gain is determined by R1 and R2 as described in section 2.2. As the frequency rises the impedance of C decreases causing the gain to fall.

The roll off frequency is given by:—

$$f = \frac{1}{2 \pi CR2}$$

5.2.2 Classical Low Pass Filter
The classical operational amplifier low pass filter is shown on Fig.5.2. This has unity gain at low frequencies. To simplify calculations, R1 and R2 should be equal, and C1 should be twice the value of C2.

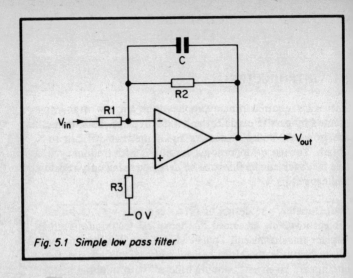

Fig. 5.1 Simple low pass filter

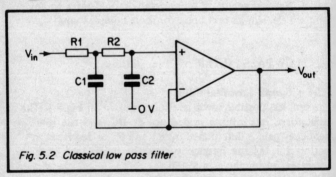

Fig. 5.2 Classical low pass filter

The cut off frequency is then given by:—

$$f = \frac{\sqrt{2}}{4 \pi \, RC}$$

If R1 = R2 = R, C2 = C and C1 = 2C.

With the relationships above the filter is said to be critically damped and the cutoff is far sharper than the simple filter of section 5.2.1. If C1 is not twice C2 the cutoff frequency is given by :—

$$f = \frac{1}{2 \pi R\sqrt{C1.C2}} \qquad \text{if } R1 = R2 = R$$

Dependent on C1 and C2 the response can be made gentle or peaky as shown on Fig.5.3.

Low pass filters similar to Fig.5.2 are the basis of audio scratch filters.

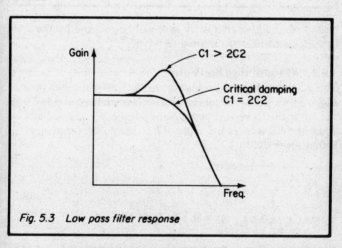

Fig. 5.3   Low pass filter response

5.3   HIGH PASS FILTERS

5.3.1   Simple High Pass Filters

The simplest high pass filter is shown on Fig.5.4. At high frequencies the gain will be determined by R1 and R2 (and the amplifier itself). At low frequencies C will have significant impedance reducing the gain. The cutoff frequency is given by:—

$$f = \frac{1}{2 \pi CR1}$$

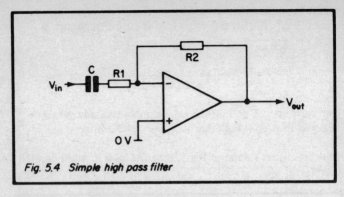

Fig. 5.4 Simple high pass filter

Note that the high frequency gain will be reduced by the limited bandwidth of the amplifier itself.

5.3.2 Classical High Pass Filter

The circuit of Fig.5.5 is identical to the low pass filter of Fig.5.2 with the capacitors and resistors interchanged. Ideally the components should be chosen such that C1 and C2 are equal and R2 is twice the value of R1. The cutoff frequency is then given by:—

$$f = \frac{\sqrt{2}}{4 \pi RC}$$

where C1 = C2 = C, R1 = R and R2 = 2R.

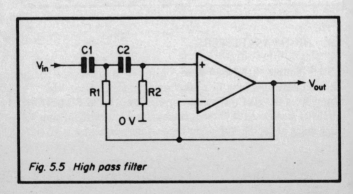

Fig. 5.5 High pass filter

The general equation with C1 = C2 = C is :—

$$f = \frac{1}{2\pi C\sqrt{(R1 \cdot R2)}}$$

with the ratio of R1 to R2 determining the response at cutoff as shown on Fig.5.6.

The high pass filter is widely used as a rumble filter in audio circuits.

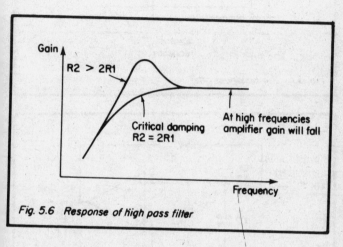

Fig. 5.6 *Response of high pass filter*

5.4 BANDPASS FILTER

5.4.1 Introduction

A bandpass filter will, as its name implies, pass a specific band of frequencies and reject frequencies higher or lower than the specified band. A bandpass filter is specified simply by two parameters; the centre frequency and the ratio of the centre frequency to the −3dB bandwidth (denoted by Q). The higher the value of Q, the sharper the shape of the curve of Fig.5.7.

5.4.2 Single Amplifier Bandpass Filters

The circuit of Fig.5.8 is widely used as a bandpass filter. To

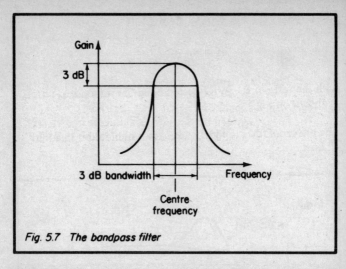

Fig. 5.7 The bandpass filter

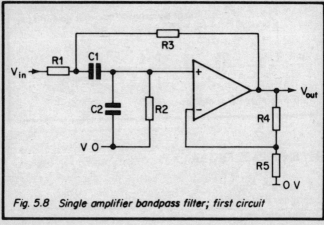

Fig. 5.8 Single amplifier bandpass filter; first circuit

simplify calculation R1, R2, R3 should be equal (denoted by R) and C1 and C2 should be equal (denoted by C). The centre frequency, fo, is then given by:—

$$fo = \frac{\sqrt{2}}{2 \pi RC}$$

86

The Q of the circuit is determined by R4 and R5 with:—

$$Q = \frac{R5\sqrt{2}}{4R5 - R4}.$$

An alternative single amplifier circuit is shown on Fig.5.9. The components should be chosen such that R1 and R2 should be equal (denoted by R) and R3 should be chosen to be 2R. C1 and C2 should be made equal (denoted by C). The equations are somewhat simpler, with:—

$$fo = \frac{1}{2\pi RC}$$

and

$$Q = \frac{R5}{2R5 - R4}$$

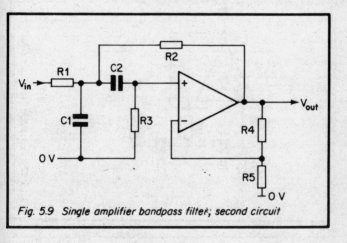

Fig. 5.9 Single amplifier bandpass filter; second circuit

5.4.3 Two Stage Bandpass Filter

The circuit of Fig.5.10 is easier to comprehend than those of the previous section, although it uses two amplifiers. IC1 is a low pass filter similar to section 5.2.1, and IC2 a high pass filter similar in principle to section 5.3.1. The centre frequency is determined by

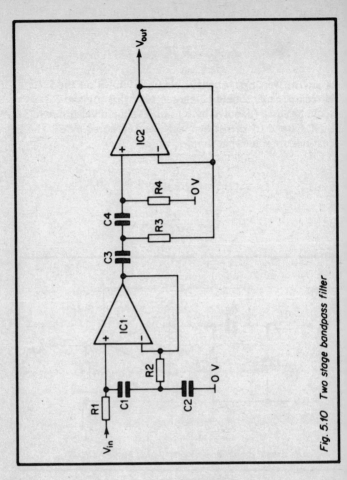

Fig. 5.10 Two stage bandpass filter

$$fo = \frac{1}{2 \pi RC}$$

if R1 = R2 = R3 = R4 = R and C1 = C2 = C3 = C4 = C.

The bandwidth is determined by the cutoff frequencies as described in sections 5.2.1 and 5.3.1. If the above equalities do not hold, the upper and lower frequency cutoff can be determined separately.

5.5 NOTCH FILTERS

5.5.1 Introduction
A notch filter is the opposite of a bandpass filter in that it rejects a band of frequencies. Commonly the notch filter is used to reject 50Hz mains hum (60Hz outside Great Britain) in sensitive audio circuits and measuring instruments. The centre frequency and Q of a notch filter are defined in a similar manner to those of a bandpass filter.

5.5.2 Single Amplifier Notch Filter
The circuit of Fig.5.11 gives a notch filter of very high Q. To simplify the design, the values should be chosen such that:—

$$R1 = R2 = R$$
$$R3 = R/2$$
$$C1 = C2 = C$$
$$C3 = 2C$$

If the above conditions are met, the centre frequency is given by:—

$$fo = \frac{1}{2 \pi RC}$$

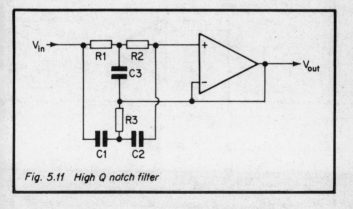

Fig. 5.11 High Q notch filter

89

5.5.3 Two Amplifier Tunable Notch Filter

The circuit of section 5.5.2 gives a short notch, but the equalities necessary make it difficult to tune. The circuit of Fig.5.12 can be tuned by a single variable capacitor, C1. Normally C1 will be a few hundred picafarads and C2 several microfarads. As usual, the design is simplified by the resistor equalities below:—

$$R1 = R2 = R3 = R$$
$$R4 = R5 = R/2$$

The centre frequency is then given by:—

$$fo = \frac{1}{\pi R \sqrt{C1C2}}$$

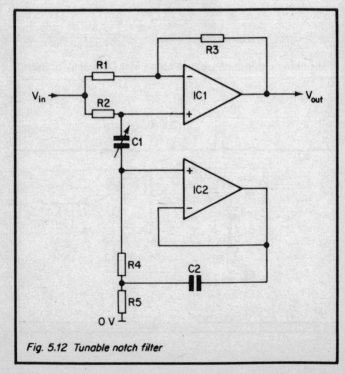

Fig. 5.12 Tunable notch filter

5.5.4 Adjustable Q Notch Filter

The circuit of Fig. 5.13 allows the Q of a notch filter to be varied by a single potentiometer without varying the centre frequency. The potentiometer can be any reasonable value, the Q of the circuit being determined by the ratio R_a/R_b. As usual, some equalities must be observed:—

$$R1 = R2 = R$$
$$R3 = R/2$$
$$C1 = C2 = C$$
$$C3 = 2C$$

The centre frequency is given by:—

$$f_o = \frac{1}{2 \pi RC}$$

The adjustable Q notch filter is very useful in low level measuring instruments.

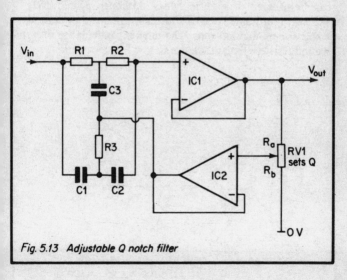

Fig. 5.13 Adjustable Q notch filter

5.6   PRACTICAL OBSERVATIONS

The obvious is sometimes overlooked, but it should be noted that in all the above equations resistors must be in OHMs and capacitors in FARADS giving results in Hz (cycles per Second for older readers!)

Where equalities are given, precision resistors (at worst 1% tolerance) should be used and close tolerance capacitors. Multiples and division by two is often needed in the equations, and this is best achieved by one value of resistor and capacitor throughout, and using parallel or series combinations to produce the multiples required.

It will often be found that none of the preferred value resistors or capacitors give the required frequency. Series combinations of resistors should be used in preference to variable resistors. This is inelegant, but one of the sad facts of life in filter design. Alternatively precision wire wound or thin film resistors can be ordered to specific values. Although prohibitively expensive for home "one-offs' this approach is economically viable for production runs. The inherent inductance of wire wound resistors limits their use to low frequency circuits.

CHAPTER 6
MISCELLANEOUS CIRCUITS

6.1 INTRODUCTION

The circuits in the previous sections fall into neat labels like,
"Audio Circuits" or "Filters". Those described in this section
do not give themselves to easy categorisation, but are nonetheless very useful circuits demonstrating the versatility of
the Operational Amplifier.

6.2 WINDOW DETECTOR

The window detector is a circuit that indicates if an input
voltage is within specified limits. It can thus be used as part
of an industrial control scheme, giving an alarm if the
measured variable (temperature, liquid level, etc.) goes outside
the correct levels. Alternatively it can be used as part of an
automatic test box for anything from resistors to power
supplies.

The circuit shown on Fig.6.1a has the response of Fig.6.1b.
With the input voltage between V_1 and V_2 the output relay is
energised. If the input voltage goes above V_1 or below V_2 the
relay de-energises. V_1 and V_2 thus determine the "correct"
range and can be any value or polarity (except, of course, the
obvious one that V_1 must be more positive than V_2!)

Amplifier IC1 is a simple inverting amplifier, to allow small
differences to be detected with reasonable values of V_1 and
V_2. The gain is adjusted by RV1. If required an offset can be
added by RV2, if it is required to have a small band on top of
a large voltage (e.g. with a correct range 5V to 5.5V, RV2 could
be used to null out 5V, allowing a gain of 20 to be used on IC1
to amplify the 0.5V band to 10 volts at IC1 output).

The output of IC1 is applied to the non-inverting input of IC2
and the inverting input of IC3. These amplifiers have no feed-

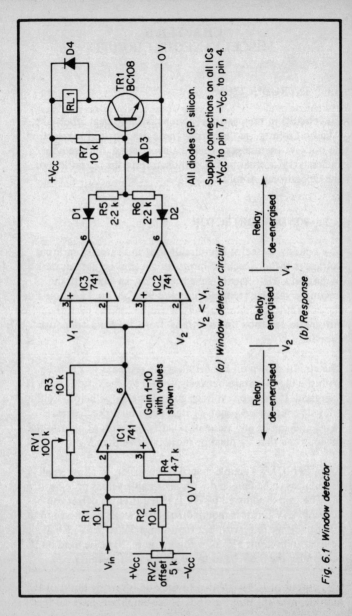

(a) Window detector circuit

All diodes GP silicon.

Supply connections on all ICs
+V_{CC} to pin 7, –V_{CC} to pin 4.

$V_2 < V_1$

(b) Response

Relay de-energised		Relay energised		Relay de-energised
	V_2		V_1	

Fig. 6.1 Window detector

94

back, and hence operate with full gain. For all practical considerations, therefore, the outputs will be at either the positive or negative supplies depending on the comparison of IC1 output with V_1 or V_2.

The outputs of IC2 and IC3 are connected to the base of TR1. With the output of IC1 between V_1 and V_2, both outputs will be positive and TR1 will be turned on with base current supplied by R7. If the output of IC1 goes more positive than V_1 or more negative than V_2 the corresponding output will go to the negative supply rail, and turning TR1 off via R5 or R6. Relay RL1 will thus de-energise if the input goes outside the predetermined range.

Possible sources for V_1 and V_2 are shown on Fig.6.2. Note that because IC1 is connected as an inverting amplifier (to allow an offset to be added), voltage V_2 corresponds to the maximum trigger voltage at R1, and V_1 to the minimum trigger voltage. Where the supply rails are of dubious stability (e.g. a battery supply) the zener diode sources are preferable.

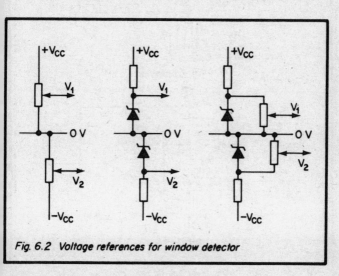

Fig. 6.2 Voltage references for window detector

6.3 VOLTAGE TO CURRENT AND CURRENT TO VOLTAGE CONVERSION

If a voltage is to be conveyed down a cable for any distance it is desirable to convert it to a current and reconvert it a voltage at the receiving end because of the superior noise rejection given by a current loop. In addition many industrial actuators and instruments require a current input.

The circuit in Fig.6.3a has a voltage input on the non-inverting input of IC1. The load is connected between the amplifier output and the inverting input, and thence to ground via R1.

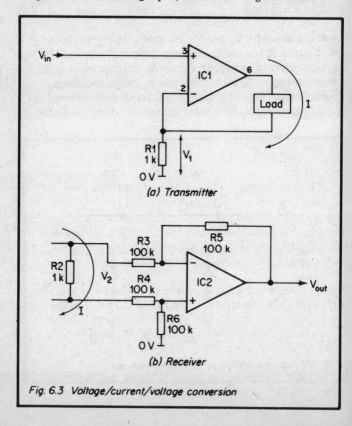

(a) Transmitter

(b) Receiver

Fig. 6.3 Voltage/current/voltage conversion

To maintain balance the amplifier output will drive a current, I, through the load and R1 producing a voltage at the inverting input of I.R1.

Since $V_1 = V_{in}$

$$I = \frac{V_{in}}{R1}$$ which is totally independent of the load.

The circuit outputs a current into the line which is solely dependent on the input signal, and independent of the load.

At the receiving end, the current can be converted to a voltage, if required, by the circuit of Fig.6.3b. The current passes through resistor R2 and produces a voltage V_2. This voltage is connected to a differential amplifier (see section 2.5) to remove any common mode noise, giving the output voltage V_{out}.

If R1 = R2 and R3 − R6 are equal, the whole circuit has unity gain and $V_{out} = V_{in}$.

6.4 RAMP CIRCUIT

In motor drive circuits the acceleration is often required to be limited to prevent excessive currents or mechanical strain. The low pass filter of section 5.2.1 will give an exponential response, but a more elegant solution is shown on Fig.6.4. This has a constant rate of change of output until $V_{out} = -V_{in}$. The response can thus be summarised as Fig.6.5.

On Fig.6.4, IC1 is used as a comparator, comparing V_{out} with V_{in}. If the non-inverting input of IC1 is positive, then the output of IC1 will be at the positive supply rail. Similarly if the non-inverting input is negative the output of IC1 will be at the negative supply rail.

R1 and R2 determine the gain of the circuit, and for unity gain are equal. IC1 will thus balance when $V_{out} = -V_{in}$.

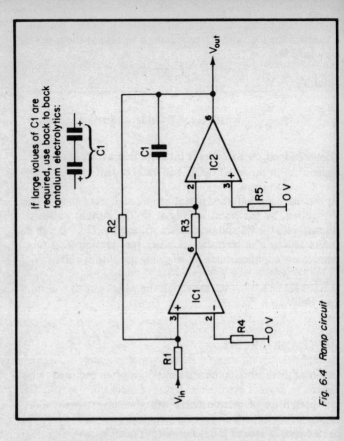

If large values of C1 are required, use back to back tantalum electrolytics:

Fig. 6.4 Ramp circuit

IC2 acts as an integrator, except the input to R3 can only be the positive supply or the negative supply. Suppose V_{in} is greater than $-V_{out}$. The input to R3 will be the positive supply, and V_{out} will change in a linear manner until V_{out} again equals $-V_{in}$. Similarly, if V_{in} is less than $-V_{out}$, we will get a linear change of V_{out} until balance is attained again. When V_{out} equals $-V_{in}$ the output of IC1 is nominally 0V, but in practice will dither randomly compensating for offset currents in the integrator.

The gain of the circuit is simply $-R2/R1$.

98

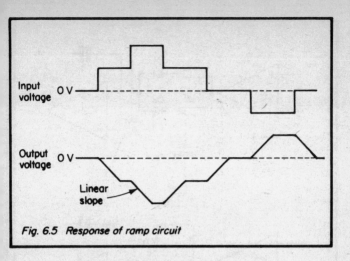

Fig. 6.5 Response of ramp circuit

The rate of change of the output is given by

$$\frac{V}{R3.C1} \quad \text{volts/second,}$$

where V is the supply rail voltages (assumed equal ±V) and R is expressed in ohms and C in farads. Alternatively R3 can be in megohms and C1 in microfarads.

If different rise and fall rates are required, either of the circuits of Fig.6.6a and b can be used. In each case R3 determines the negative output ramp rate, and R4 the positive rate, with the above equation still applicable. Fig.6.6b has the advantage that V_1 and V_2 need not be the supply rails, and could be derived from elsewhere.

6.5   PHASE ADVANCE CIRCUIT

The phase advance circuit is almost the opposite of the ramp circuit. It is used to "kick" an output before settling down to the final value as shown on Fig.6.7b. It is very useful for starting motors connected to loads with high inertia.

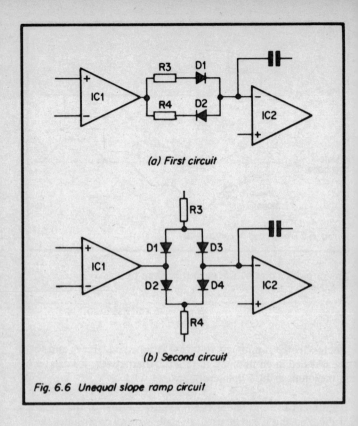

(a) First circuit

(b) Second circuit

Fig. 6.6 Unequal slope ramp circuit

The circuit is shown on Fig.6.7a. In the steady state condition it behaves as a normal inverting amplifier with gain determined by R1, R2, R3. As the input changes, however, C1 delays the feedback causing the output spike. As C1 charges, the output returns to the steady state value. The depth of the spike is determined by the ratio of R4 to R2 and R3, and the duration by C1 multiplied by R2, R3, R4 in parallel.

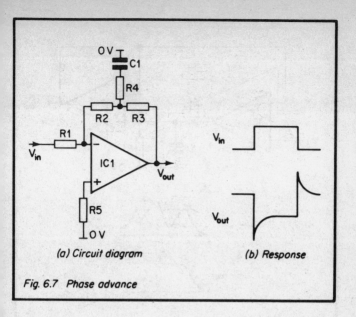

(a) Circuit diagram   *(b) Response*

Fig. 6.7 Phase advance

6.6   PEAK PICKER

The circuit of Fig.6.8 can be used to store the peak value of a
varying signal. It is thus useful for level indicators in audio
work and many aspects of industrial control.

If the input voltage is greater than the output voltage, the output of IC1 will go positive charging C1 until the output voltage
and input voltage are equal. When the input voltage falls, the
output of IC1 goes negative but D1 stops C1 discharging. The
voltage on C1 (and the output voltage) is thus the maximum
attained by the input.

The voltage on C1 will slowly decay due to the input bias
current of IC2. If a long storage time is required IC2 should be
one of the FET amplifiers. If R1 is added the voltage on C1
will decay at a fixed rate, indicating the maximum value
attained over the last few seconds (the actual time being deter-

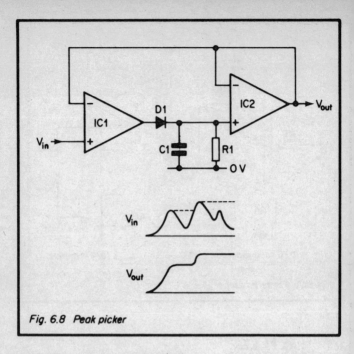

Fig. 6.8 Peak picker

mined by the time constant R1C1).

If D1 is reversed, the circuit stores the minimum (or most negative) input voltage.

6.7 SAMPLE AND HOLD

The sample and hold circuit is a variation on the peak picker of section 6.6. The sample and hold is used to "freeze" a varying signal by taking a snapshot picture. The resulting stable voltage can then be measured without ambiguity.

The basis is shown on Fig.6.9. With SW1 closed, the voltage on C1 and the output voltage will equal the input voltage as described in the previous section. If SW1 is open, C1 will hold the voltage at the instant the switch opened. In a sample and hold

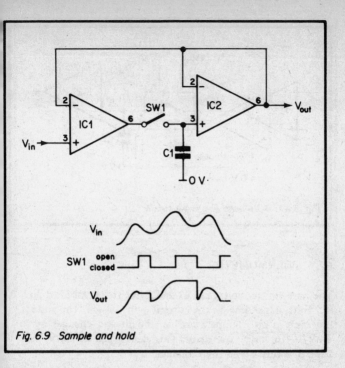

Fig. 6.9 Sample and hold

circuit, SW1 is normally open and is closed briefly to obtain a
sample.

SW1 can be any form of switch. Reed relays were often used
(and still are in some applications) but the solid state switches
provided by FETs are ideally suited. Fig.6.10 shows a circuit
using the popular 4016 CMOS switch. The circuit shown
allows any voltage between 1 volt and 14 volts to be stored.
More expensive switches are available (e.g. the 7502) which
can be used with two supply rails.

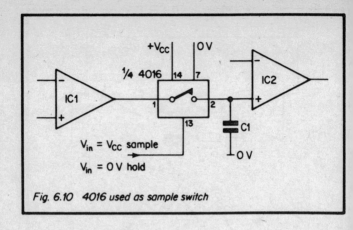

Fig. 6.10 4016 used as sample switch

6.8   THERMOMETER

The base-emitter voltage of a conducting transistor is around 0.5 volts, depending on the current being passed. The voltage, however, is also temperature dependent and changes by 2mV/°C for every transistor. This change can be made the basis of a very useful thermometer.

The circuit is shown on Fig.6.11. The temperature probe is TR1, biased into conduction by R1, R2 and RV1. The resulting base-emitter voltage is connected to the non-inverting input of IC1, which is connected as a non-inverting amplifier with gain adjustable around 50. The inverting input is biased at about 0.5 volts negative by R4, R3 and RV2.

RV2 acts, therefore, as a coarse zero control and RV1 as a fine zero control by varying the current through TR1. To set the zero, the probe should be immersed in melting ice and RV2 and RV1 adjusted for zero reading on the meter.

The probe should then be immersed in boiling water and RV3 set for 10 volts at the meter. The meter now reads 0 − 10 volts for 0 − 100°C.

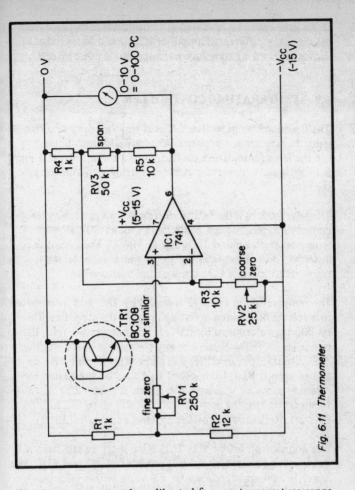

Fig. 6.11 Thermometer

The thermometer can be calibrated for any temperature range, but remember that transistors will be destroyed at temperatures in excess of 150°C.

The −15 volt rail must be well stabilised since the biasing for the non-inverting input is derived from this rail. The positive rail can be any value in the range 6 volts to 15 volts and need not be particularly well stabilised.

If the probe is to be mounted at a considerable distance from the circuit, a differential amplifier IC2 should be included as shown on Fig.6.12 to reduce common mode noise effects.

6.9   TEMPERATURE CONTROLLER

The thermometer in section 6.8 used the V_{BE} drop of a transistor to measure temperature. An alternative technique is to use the large temperature coefficient of a thermistor, and Fig. 6.13 shows a temperature controller using a thermistor as the sensor.

The resistance of a thermistor decreases with increasing temperature, a typical device going from around 10k at room temperature to around 100ohms at 100°C. The response is, however, non linear making them more suitable for temperature control than temperature measurement.

The temperature in Fig.6.13 is sensed by Th1, and is converted to a voltage on the non-inverting input of the amplifier. The set point is determined by RV1. If the temperature falls, the resistance of Th1 will increase and the voltage at R1 will rise. The output of the amplifier will go positive turning TR1 on and energising RL1. Contacts of RL1 turn on the heater, circulation pump or whatever the circuit is controlling. On a temperature fall, the amplifier output will go to 0V, turning TR1 off. Resistor R6 provides hysteresis to prevent jitter.

The comparison bridge R1, Th1, RV1 must be fed from a stable voltage source, and this is provided by R7 and ZD1. The Zener is deliberately chosen at 5.6 volts at this value has practically zero temperature coefficient itself.

Thermistors are available for many temperature ranges, and with care control to better than 2°C can be obtained.

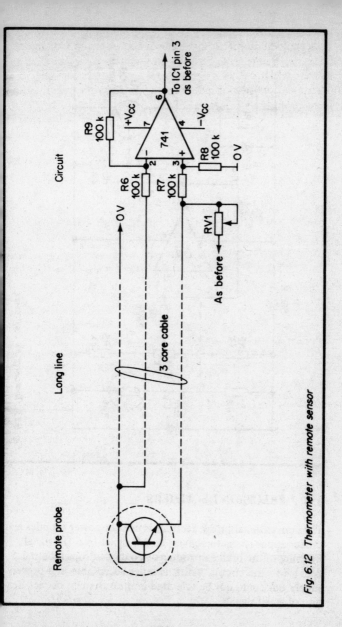

Fig. 6.12 Thermometer with remote sensor

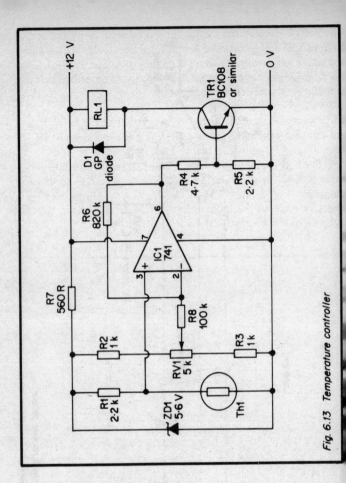

Fig. 6.13 Temperature controller

6.10 PRECISION RECTIFIERS

The conventional bridge rectifier is used in power supplies and similar applications to convert an AC signal to a DC signal. In doing so the bridge introduces two diode drops (about 1.5 volts) into the circuit, which is quite acceptable in a power supply but could not be tolerated in measurement or rectification of small signals.

The voltage drop across the diodes can be reduced by the open loop gain of an Operational Amplifier if the diodes are used in the amplifier feedback. There are many possible ways of obtaining perfect rectification, but the circuit described below is probably the easiest to understand.

First we must consider the halfwave rectifier of Fig.6.14. This is a conventional inverting amplifier with the inclusion of D1 and D2, and R1 and R2 equal in value. When V_{in} is on the negative half cycle, $V_{out} = -V_{in}$ by the arguments outlined in section 2.2. Note that the actual output of voltage of the amplifier, V_o, will be offset by the diode drop. During the negative cycle of the input we therefore get a positive half cycle output voltage with no voltage drop.

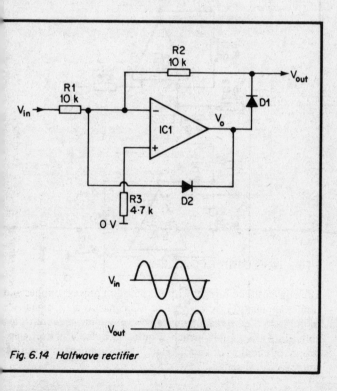

Fig. 6.14 Halfwave rectifier

On the positive input cycle, the amplifier output goes negative back biasing D1. Diode D2 stops the amplifier from saturating, keeping V_o at around 0.8 volts negative. V_o is now connected to the virtual earth by R2, giving zero output volts. The output over one complete cycle is a halfwave rectified version of the input.

Fig.6.15 is an additional amplifier, and gives full wave rectification. IC1 is a half wave rectifier similar to 6.14 except D1 and D2 have been reversed to give a negative output. IC2 is

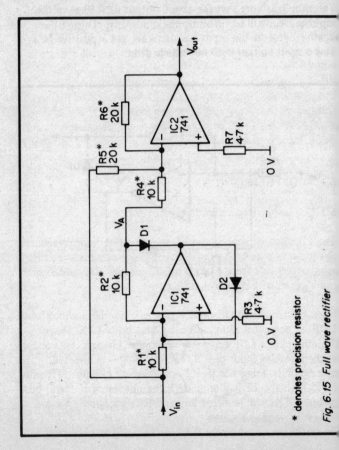

* denotes precision resistor

Fig. 6.15 Full wave rectifier

110

a conventional inverting adder, summing the input voltage V_{in} and the output of IC1. Note, however, that R5 = R6 = 2R4. V_{out} is therefore given by:—

$$V_{out} = -(V_{in} + 2V_A).$$

When V_{in} is on the positive half cycle, $V_A = -V_{in}$, so $V_{out} = V_{in}$. When V_{in} is on the negative half cycle, $V_A = 0$, so $V_{out} = -V_{in}$, i.e. a positive output.

The output is thus a perfect full wave rectified version of the input signal with no diode drops.

The maximum frequency at which the circuit will operate is mainly determined by the slew rate of IC1. As the input goes through zero, IC1 output has to swing by two diode drops. If this time is significant compared with the period of the waveform, distortion will result at the zero crossing points. If amplifiers with fast slew rates are used, operation at frequencies over 200kHz is feasible.

6.11   OPTOELECTRONICS

6.11.1   Light Dependent Resistors

The LDR is the cheapest optical sensor and in many respects the most versatile. They exhibit a change of resistance of around 100 to 1 from dark to bright illumination, and as such can be used with simple circuits.

Fig.6.16 shows an LDR used as part of a burglar alarm. The LDR is normally illuminated by the bulb LP1. When illuminated the LDR has a low resistance, giving a low voltage at the inverting input of IC1. The Op Amp is connected as a Schmitt Trigger with R2 and R3 determining UTP and LTP. With the LDR illuminated, the output of IC1 will be positive, TR1 will be turned on and RL1 energised.

When the beam is broken, the resistance of the LDR rises and

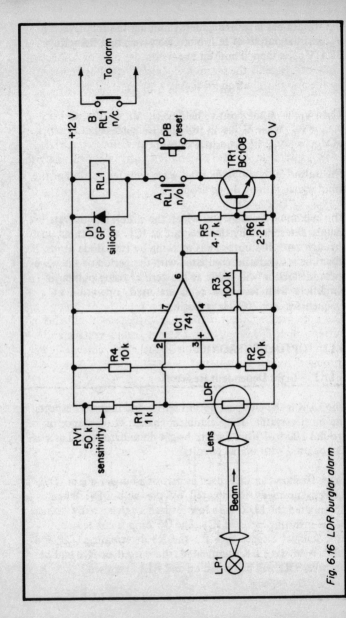

Fig. 6.16 LDR burglar alarm

the voltage at the inverting input rises above UTP, and IC1 output switches to 0V, turning TR1 off and de-energising RL1. Once dropped out, RL1 stays out because of contact A. Contact B sounds the alarm bell. Initially RL1 is energised by the arm push button PB1.

The variable resistor RV1 sets the circuit sensitivity. For maximum range, LDR and LP1 should be placed at the focus of a converging lens or a parabolic mirror (from a torch). If LDR is interchanged with R1 and RV1, the relay will energise when the beam is broken.

6.11.2 Photodiodes

Photodiodes are normal diodes operated with reverse bias. As usual a small leakage current flows, but in a photodiode this leakage current varies linearly with light. Fig.6.17 is a circuit to convert this leakage current change to a useful voltage which can be read on a meter or fed to a Schmitt Trigger similar to the preceeding section.

The non-inverting input of IC1 is a virtual earth, but the current input is derived from D1, not from a voltage and resistor as usual. To maintain the virtual earth, current flows through R1, and.—

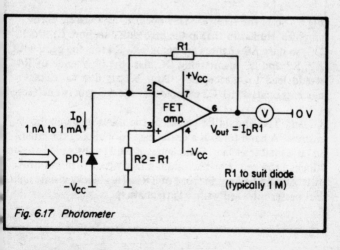

Fig. 6.17 Photometer

$$V_{out} = I_D R1.$$

The resistor R1 thus determines the gain of the circuit.

Because the currents involved are small (typically 1nA to 1mA) the amplifier needs to have low input bias current. The circuit works particularly well with FET input amplifiers.

6.11.3   Optical Link
The final optical sensor is the phototransistor. This is similar to the photodiode in that the leakage current of the transistor varies with incident light. The change in leakage current in the phototransistor is, however, far greater than that in the photodiode.

As a demonstration of the use of the phototransistor, Fig. 6.18a and b shows an experimental optical speech link. No one would seriously suggest this is any better than the field phones of section 4.2, but it is an interesting "fun" circuit.

Fig.6.18a is the transmitter, and is essentially a V to I converter, changing the voltage changes at the microphone to current changes through the Infra Red LED. For a 20mV signal, the current through the diode will change by 20mA.

Fig.6.18b is the receiver. This operates as a virtual earth amplifier similar to that in the preceeding section. C1 blocks DC, so only AC changes are amplified. R4 sets the gain, with R2, R3 and C3 maintaining DC bias (the high value of R4 would lead to unacceptably large offsets due to leakage currents on its own). C2 ensures that the AC gain is unaffected.

D1 and TR1 should be placed at the focus of parabolic mirrors. A hand torch is a useful case for building the circuit in, as a matter of fact. Glass lenses should be discarded as glass blocks infra red. For maximum sensitivity, a Wrattan 88A filter should be used in front of TR1. This blocks visible light, but passes infra red without attenuation.

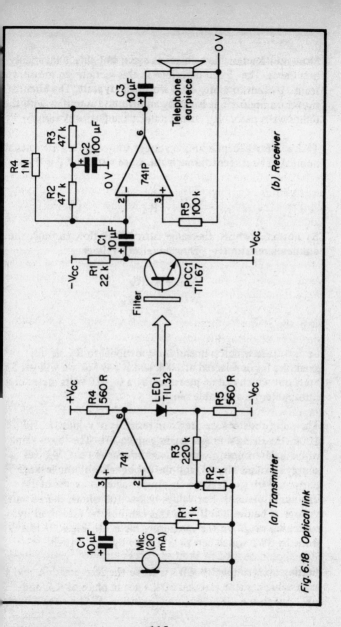

Fig. 6.18 Optical link

115

6.12 LINEAR OHMETER

Most multimeters have an ohms scale, but this is invariably non linear. The circuit described in this section can measure from 10 ohms to 1 Meg ohm with a linear scale. The circuit, shown on Fig.6.19, is basically an inverting amplifier with the unknown resistor, R_X, being used at the feedback resistor.

TR1 and RV1 form a simple voltage source, giving 10 volts at point A. The current through the range resistor R_A is then:—

$$I_1 = \frac{10}{R_A}.$$

By normal analysis, the same current will flow through the unknown resistor R_X, giving an output voltage:—

$$V_{out} = I_1.R_X$$
$$= -10\frac{R_X}{R_A}$$

i.e. a voltage which is linearly proportional to R_X. If, for example, R_A is selected at 100k and R_X is 56k we will get 5.6 volts out which can be measured by a $0 - 10$ volts meter or a multimeter on a suitable range.

The range resistors are precision resistors of values 1k, 10k, 100k, 1M giving 4 ranges reading up to 1M. The lower value of 1k is determined by the maximum current the 741 can supply (around 10mA), and the upper value by the leakage current. With low leakage Op Amps values in excess of 1M can easily be used. For values below 100 ohms, the output voltage is below 1 volt, and this can best be measured by switching range on the measuring meter. In Fig.6.19 this is done by SW2 which acts as a "Divide by ten" switch.

Setting up is simplicity. SW1 is set to the zero position, and a high value resistor (around 500k) put in place of R_X, and SW2 put to the "Divide by ten" position. RV2 is then adjuste

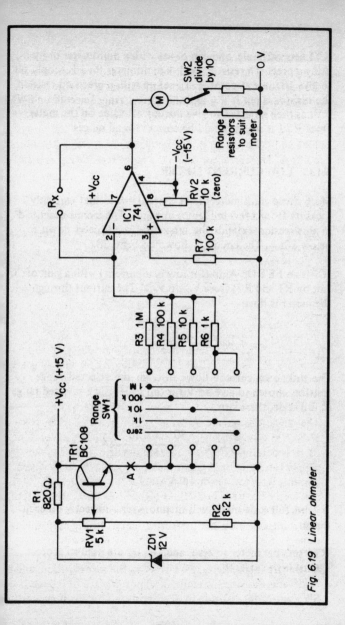

Fig. 6.19 Linear ohmeter

for zero on the meter.

RV1 sets full scale, and can be set with a multimeter or by using a precision resistor. With a multimeter RV1 is simply set to give 10 volts at point A. To set up with a precision resistor, the resistor is put in R_X and the correct range selected on SW1. RV1 is then adjusted to give the correct value on the meter. Once RV1 is set, it should be correct for all ranges.

6.13   LOW CURRENT METER

Most cheap multimeters have current scales that can only measure from a few milliamps upwards. The circuit described in this section extends the range of a multimeter down to below $10\mu A$. The circuit is shown on Fig.6.20.

IC1 is an FET Op Amp (for low bias current) with a gain of 50 (set by R1 and R2) from V_{in} to V_{out}. The current through the meter is thus:—

$$I_{out} = 50 . \frac{V_{in}}{R3}$$

The unknown current flows through the selected range resistor, chosen to give 5mV for full scale. For a selected range at full scale, therefore:—

$$I_{out} = \frac{50 \times 5 \times 10^{-3}}{250} A$$

$$= 1mA$$

A 1mA full scale meter will therefore read correctly on each range.

RV1 sets the meter to zero, and D1, D2 are used to protect against high currents.

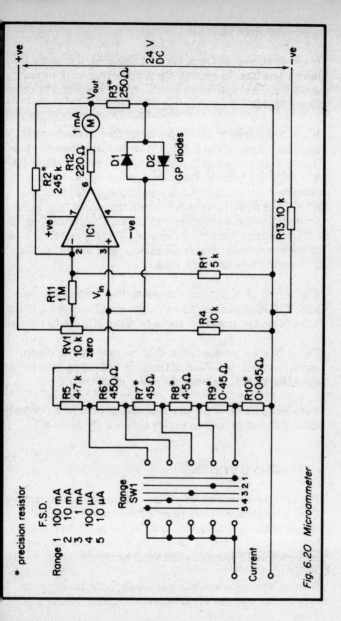

Fig. 6.20 Microammeter

* precision resistor

Range	F.S.D.
1	100 mA
2	10 mA
3	1 mA
4	100 µA
5	10 µA

119

6.14   OP AMP TESTER

If a large number of Op Amps are being used, it is useful to have a test box. In general, Op Amps either work or fail totally, and a simple go/no go test will suffice. Fig.6.21 shows such a circuit.

IC2 is the amplifier under test, connected as an inverting amplifier of gain about 0.8. IC1 is an oscillator, constructed from the ubiquitous 555, with period of 1 sec (details of the 555 timer are given in the author's book IC555 Projects, available from Bernard Babani (publishing) Ltd; Book No. BP44). The output oscillates between the supply rails, and is connected to the input resistor of the amplifier under test. If IC2 is operating correctly its output will swing to within a volt of the supply rails. This is deliberate, since some amplifiers latch up if driven into saturation.

The output of IC2 drives a non-inverting buffer IC3, since some CMOS amplifiers can only drive a milliamp or so. If any 741 and similar amplifiers are to be tested IC2 can be omitted

Two LEDs are connected to IC2 output. As the output oscillates these will flash alternately indicating correct operation of IC1, the amplifier under test.

Note that because of the pin compatability between Op Amps the circuit can be used to test all common Op Amps ICs.

6.15   SERVO SYSTEMS

The two servo systems below are position control systems. They have an input comprising a hand turned dial, and a remote indicator which the unit drives to the same position. Position controls similar to this are widely used for remote indication and application like aerial rotators.

Both of the servo systems use simple potentiometers to measure the position of the input unit (called the transmitter,

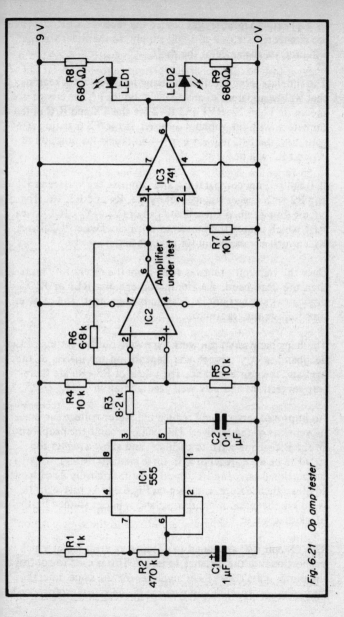

Fig. 6.21 Op amp tester

or TX) and the remote unit (called the receiver, or R/C). These are connected across a ±15 volt supply, so the slider voltage will indicate the angle of the shaft.

The simplest servo is called the Bang-bang servo, for reasons that will be apparent to anyone who builds it! The circuit is shown on Fig.6.22. RV1 and RV2 are the TX and R/C potentiometers, with the supplies reversed. If the TX is sitting at +4 volts, say, the R/C will drive to −4 volts and the junction of R1 and R2 will be zero.

IC1 and IC2 are comparators, and compare the voltage at R1 and R2 with trigger voltages set by R3, R4 and R5, R6. The circuit thus exhibits a deadband gap of $(V_1 - V_2)$. IC1 drives RL1 which causes the motor to drive clockwise. IC2 drives RL2 which causes the motor to drive anticlockwise.

Once the transmitter moves away from the receiver by more than the dead band, the circuit will energise RL1 or RL2 driving the receiver until it is again in alignment. The receiver thus follows the transmitter.

The Bang-bang servo can work very well, but the setting of the deadband is very critical, and depends on the inertia of the load and the gear box ratio. The values of R3−R6 are therefore suggestions and may well need alteration.

An improved servo would reduce the motor voltage for small movements of the receiver. This will overcome the propensity of the Bang-bang servo to oscillate, and allow a higher top speed to be used. A servo with these characteristics is called a proportional servo, and a typical circuit, originally developed to illustrate a lecture, is shown on Fig.6.24. At first sight this is, to say the least, awe inspiring, and is better studied by the block diagram of Fig.6.23.

The TX and R/C are added to produce an error signal which is proportional to the distance to target. This is used to control the motor volts via a power amplifier. At the same time, the desired motor speed is compared with the actual motor speed

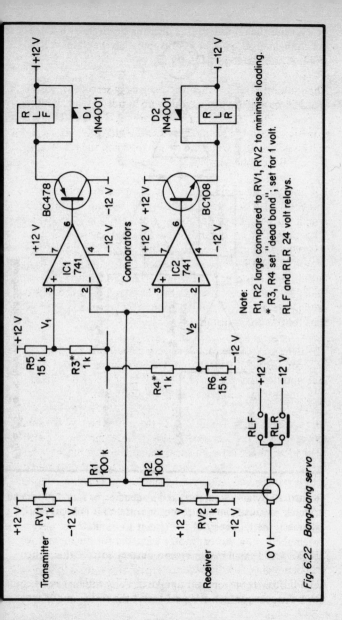

Note:
R1, R2 large compared to RV1, RV2 to minimise loading.
* R3, R4 set "dead band"; set for 1 volt.
RLF and RLR 24 volt relays.

Fig. 6.22 Bang-bang servo

123

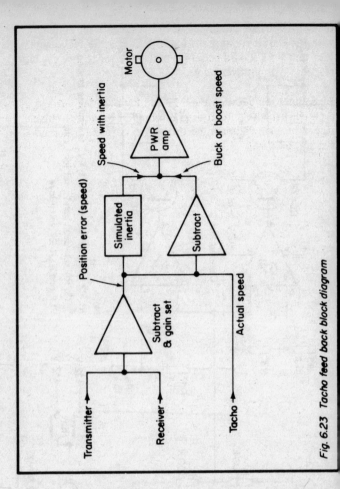

Fig. 6.23 Tacho feed back block diagram

(measured by a tachometer) and a speed error signal produced to buck or boost the actual motor volts. This reduces considerably the tendency of the circuit to oscillate. In the original circuit a slot car motor was used for the main drive motor, and a small motor from a battery toy for the tacho.

RV5 is a zero control used to take out any misalignment, and RV1 the gain control. RV2 calibrates the tacho, and is set such that zero volts are obtained out of the speed error amplifier with the motor running off load. RV3 sets the tacho gain. RV1 and RV3 should be set by trial and error to give the best response without overshoot.

By comparison between Fig.6.23 and Fig.6.24 the purpose of each IC in the full circuit diagram should be readily available. IC3 and C2 simulate the inertia of a heavy load for demonstration purposes.

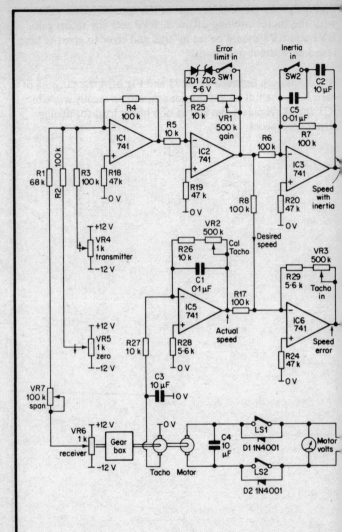

Fig. 6.24 Proportional servo system

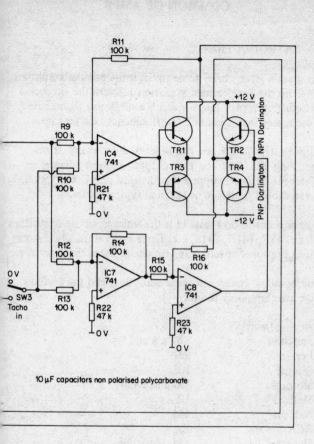

10 μF capacitors non polarised polycarbonate

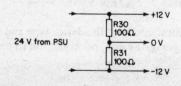

CHAPTER 7
COMMON OP AMPS

7.1 INTRODUCTION

This section gives a brief guide to the more popular amplifiers. The terms used are defined in section 1.3 with the exception of Useful Frequency range which is a subjective figure based on use rather than a specific gain/frequency relationship.

Although Op Amps are manufactured by many firms, assembling the data for this chapter showed surprising differences between supposedly identical chips. The figures quoted should therefore be taken as typical values.

Another point to take note of is the widespread use of suffixes such as 741C, 741N, 741S, etc. These suffixes usually denote tight or improved specification on one or more characteristics.

Manufacturers' codes can cause confusion, and the prefixes below are commonly found:—

Analog Devices	AD
Fairchild	LM, μA and U
Ferranti	ZN
Intersil	ICL
Motorola	MC and MLM
Mullard	UL
National	LM
RCA	CA
Signetics	LM, N and NE
Texas Instruments	SN72 or SN52

These prefixes are combined with the device type and sundry suffixes denote temperature range, packaging etc to produce labels like:—

ICL741CTY

7.2 OPERATIONAL AMPLIFIERS

7.2.1 741

Supply voltage	±3V min, ±18V max
Max differential input voltage	30V
Open loop gain	106dB
Input resistance	2M
Offset voltage	2mV
Offset current	20nA
Bias Current	80nA
Slew rate	0.5V/μS
Offset voltage temp coeff	5μV/°C
CMRR	90dB
Useful frequency range	10kHz

Comments

Good cheap general purpose amplifier;

Unconditionally stable,

Many close relatives (e.g. low noise, high slew rate) with
    suffixes (e.g. 741C, 741N, 741S),

Do not short null pins to 0V. .

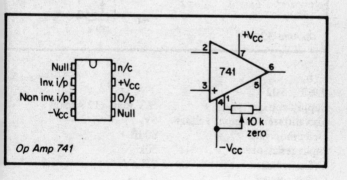

Op Amp 741

7.2.2 301

Supply voltage	±5V min, ±18V max
Max differential input voltage	30V
Open loop gain	106dB
Input resistance	2M

Offset voltage	2mV
Offset current	3nA
Bias current	70nA
Slew rate	1V/μS
Offset voltage temp coeff	5μV/°C
CMRR	90dB
Useful frequency range	50kHz

Comments
Similar to 741, with external frequency compensation as
shown.

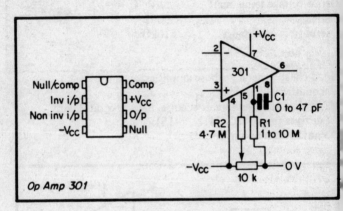

Op Amp 301

7.2.3   702

Supply voltage	±6V min, ±12V max
Max differential input voltage	5V
Open loop gain	80dB
Input resistance	50k
Offset voltage	0.7mV
Offset current	0.2μA
Bias current	2μA
Slew rate	4V/μS
Offset voltage temp coeff	3μV/°C
CMRR	95dB
Useful frequency range	10MHz

An early Op Amp IC and inferior to more modern devices;
External frequency compensation required;
Very high frequency response.

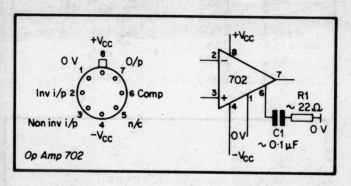

Op Amp 702

7.2.4   709

Supply voltage	±9V min, ±18V max
Max differential input voltage	5V
Open loop gain	93dB
Input resistance	250k
Offset voltage	2mV
Offset current	$0.1\mu A$
Bias current	$0.3\mu A$
Slew rate	$10V/\mu S$
Offset voltage temp coeff	$4\mu V/°C$
CMRR	90dB
Useful frequency range	1MHz

Comments

Original Op Amp IC, and as such is inferior to more modern
    devices;
Has some quirks, notably its tendency to latch up if output
    goes within 1.5V of supply rails;
Can be difficult to stabilize, if used at high frequencies;
External frequency compensation as shown.

131

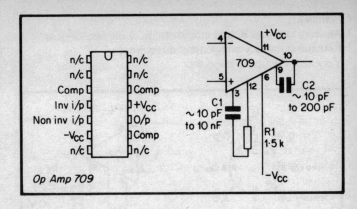

Op Amp 709

7.2.5　308

Supply voltage	±2V min, ±18V max
Max differential input voltage	30V
Open loop gain	102dB
Input resistance	40M
Offset voltage	7mV
Offset current	1nA
Bias current	5nA
Slew rate	0.2V/μS
Offset voltage temp coeff	5μV/°C
CMRR	100dB
Useful frequency range	10kHz

Op Amp 308

7.2.6   725

Supply voltage	±4V min, ±20V max
Max differential input voltage	5V
Open loop gain	127dB
Input resistance	1.5M
Offset voltage	2mV
Offset current	1.2nA
Bias current	80nA
Slew rate	$0.25V/\mu S$
Offset voltage temp coeff	$2\mu V/°C$
CMRR	115dB
Useful frequency range	1MHz

Comments

High performance, low drift amplifier, with correspondingly
   inflated price;
External frequency compensation as shown.

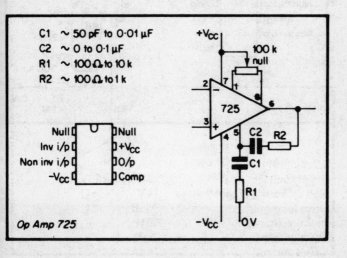

C1 ~ 50 pF to 0·01 μF
C2 ~ 0 to 0·1 μF
R1 ~ 100 Ω to 10 k
R2 ~ 100 Ω to 1 k

Op Amp 725

7.2.7 748

Supply voltage	±3V min, ±18 max
Max differential input voltage	30V
Open loop gain	106dB
Input resistance	2M
Offset voltage	2mV
Offset current	20nA
Bias current	80nA
Slew rate	0.5V/μS
Offset voltage temp coeff	5μV/°C
CMRR	90dB
Useful frequency range	50KHz

Comments
Similar to the 741 with external frequency components;
Low noise.

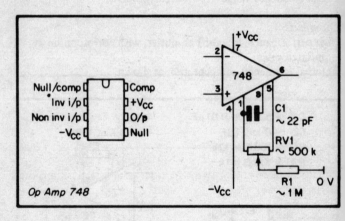

Op Amp 748

7.2.8 531

Supply voltage	±5V min, ±20V max
Max differential input voltage	15V
Open loop gain	96dB
Input resistance	20M
Offset voltage	2mV
Offset current	50nA

Bias current	400nA
Slew rate	35V/μS
Offset voltage temp coeff	10μV/$^\circ$C
CMRR	100dB
Useful frequency range	> 1MHz

Comments
Very fast slew rate and large frequency range;
External frequency compensation.

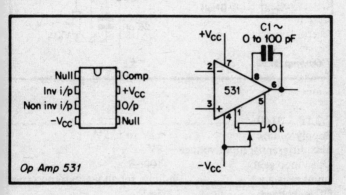

Op Amp 531

7.2.9   3130

Supply voltage	±3V min, ±8V max
Max differential input voltage	8V
Open loop gain	110dB
Input resistance	infinite for all practical purposes
Offset voltage	8mV
Offset current	0.5pA
Bias current	5pA
Slew rate	10V/μS
Offset voltage temp coeff	10μV/$^\circ$C
CMRR	80dB
Useful frequency range	50kHz

Comments
MOSFET amplifier;
External frequency compensation;

135

Can operate with $-V_{CC} = 0V$

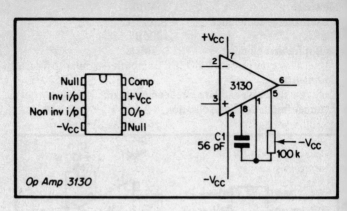

Op Amp 3130

7.2.10   3140

Supply voltage	±2V to ±15V
Max differential input voltage	8V
Open loop gain	100dB
Input resistance	infinite for all practical purposes
Offset voltage	5mV
Offset current	0.5pA
Bias current	15pA
Slew rate	10V/µS

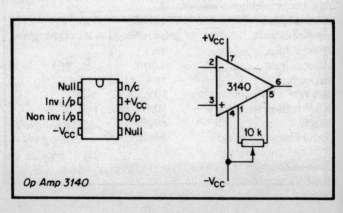

Op Amp 3140

Offset voltage temp coeff	$8\mu V/°C$
CMRR	90dB
Useful frequency range	50kHz

Comments
Internally compensated MOSFET amplifier, similar to 741.

7.2.11   ICL 7611
Supply voltage	$\pm0.5V$ to $\pm8V$
Max differential input voltage	15mV
Open loop gain	100dB*
Input resistance	effectively infinite
Offset voltage	12mV
Offset current	0.5pA
Bias current	1pA
Slew rate	$0.5V/\mu S$*
Offset voltage temp coeff	$25\mu V/°C$
CMRR	90dB*
Useful frequency range	10kHz*

*Depends on value of I_Q

Comments
CMOS amplifier with adjustable consumption;
Remarkably low supply rails.

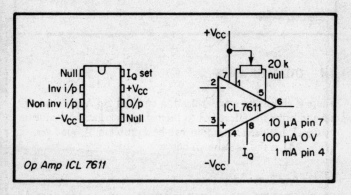

Op Amp ICL 7611

7.2.12 Other Op Amps

101   Close relative of 301;

201   Close relative of 301;

108   Close relative of 308;

208   Close relative of 308;

459   Low noise version of 741, with tight gain spec;

3030   14 pin Op Amp similar to 709 with non standard pinning.

7.3   DUAL OP AMPS

There is much less standardisation on dual Op Amps.
Commonest is the 747 which is a dual 741 in a 14 pin DIL.

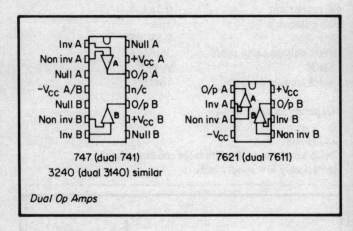

747 (dual 741)
3240 (dual 3140) similar

7621 (dual 7611)

Dual Op Amps

7.4   QUAD OP AMPS

There is almost no standardisation on quad Op Amps, and all
have inferior specifications to their single brothers. Separation
of signals between amplifiers can be a problem. A quad version
of the 741 is the 348 shown below.

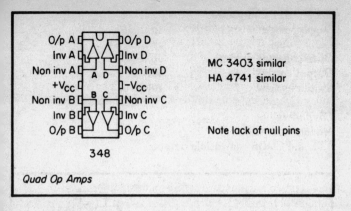

O/p A — Inv A — Non inv A — +V_CC — Non inv B — Inv B — O/p B — O/p D — Inv D — Non inv D — −V_CC — Non inv C — Inv C — O/p C

MC 3403 similar
HA 4741 similar

Note lack of null pins

348

Quad Op Amps

7.5 COMPARATORS

7.5.1 710 Comparator

Supply	+12V, −6V
Output levels	+3V, −0.5V
Switching time	100nS

Comments

Original comparator, still widely used despite its odd supply
rails.

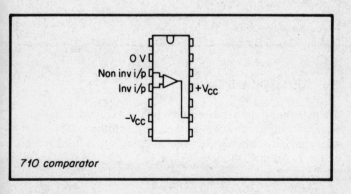

O V
Non inv i/p
Inv i/p
−V_CC
+V_CC

710 comparator

7.5.2 311 Comparator

Supply, single	up to 36V
dual	up to ±18V
Open collector output	up to 40V
Output current	40mA
Switching time	100nS

Comments

Modern comparator;
TTL and CMOS compatible outputs.

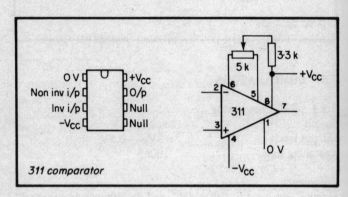

311 comparator

CHAPTER 8
POWER SUPPLIES

8.1 INTRODUCTION

The power supply requirements for Op Amps are unusual in
that two supplies are needed, one positive and one negative.
These supplies can be obtained from many sources as
described in the section following.

8.2 SUPPLIES FOR OPERATIONAL AMPLIFIERS

8.2.1 Batteries

In many applications a simple two battery supply is adequate
if the reduced ±9 volt rail can be tolerated. In most circuits the
current drawn by the Op Amps themselves will be negligible
by comparison with the current drawn by the rest of the
circuit. If two batteries are used, both supplies should be
switched by the On/Off switch.

8.2.2 Unregulated Supplies

Op Amps are relatively immune to supply variations providing
the supplies themselves are not used as part of a zeroing adjustment or voltage reference. In these less stringent applications,
a simple transformer/rectifier/capacitor circuit will suffice.
There are many possible arrangements for transformers with
separate windings and centre taps shown on Fig.8.1. Wherever
mains voltages are used, normal precautions should be taken
against electric shock.

8.2.3 Zener Regulation

Where a few Op Amps are used, simple (and cheap) regulation
can be obtained by two zener diodes as shown on Fig.8.2a.
The input voltages can be derived from any of the circuits in
Fig.8.1. Zeners can also be used to split a single supply as
Fig.8.2b.

Resistors R1 and R2 determine the bias current of the zeners,

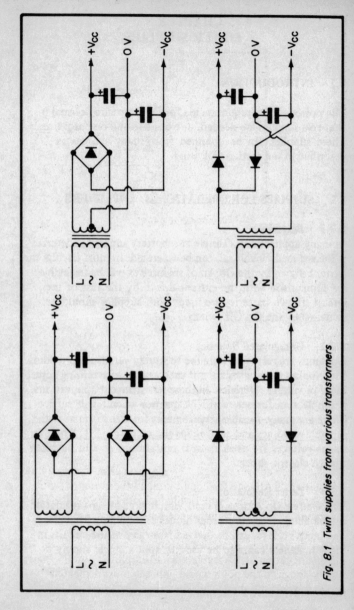

Fig. 8.1 Twin supplies from various transformers

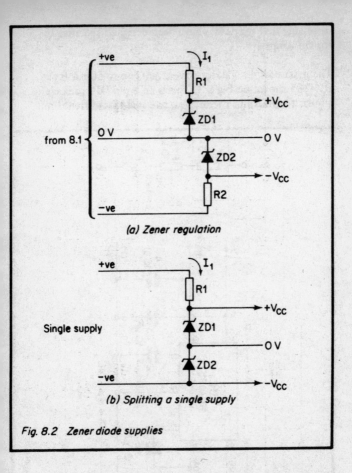

(a) Zener regulation

(b) Splitting a single supply

Fig. 8.2 Zener diode supplies

and should be chosen such that I_1 is greater than the maximum load current. In the no load condition, all the current I_1 will flow through the zener, which will dissipate $I_1 \cdot V_Z$ watts. The minimum load thus determines the zener wattage needed.

8.2.4 Integrated Circuit Regulators

The introduction of IC regulators has simplified power supply design to the point where only the most dedicated designer would build one with discrete components. It is not surprising that regulators have been designed specifically for Op Amps.

The most useful regulator for currents up to 50mA is the RC4195 shown on Fig.8.3. This is an 8 pin DIL package similar to Op Amps themselves, and includes current limit

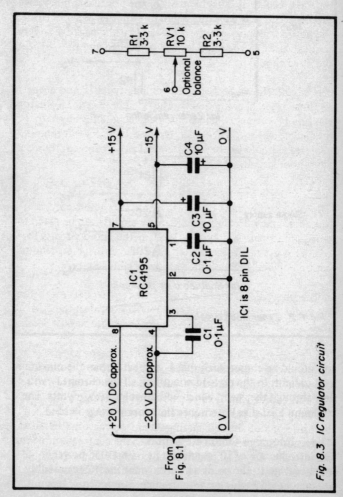

Fig. 8.3 IC regulator circuit

and thermal shutdown. Pin 6 on the IC is used to balance the two outputs if required, and can be used to offset the output if an assymetrical supply is needed.

The circuit of Fig.8.3 is useful for small systems, but can only provide up to 50mA on each rail. For larger systems, separate regulators must be used for the positive and negative supplies. The most versatile regulators are the 78 series (for the positive supply) and the 79 series (for the negative supply). In most cases 15 volt supplies will be needed and the 7815 and the 7915 should be used.

The circuit, shown on Fig.8.4, is simplicity itself, and needs minimal external components. The 78 and 79 series regulators can supply 1 Amp, which should be adequate for any reasonable system. When operated near their current limit, heat sinks should be used for the regulators although they do have internal thermal shutdown.

8.2.5 Single Supply Operation

The two supply rails of an Op Amp are, admittedly, a nuisance, and with a bit of care many circuits can be made to work on a single supply rail. Most of the audio circuits in section 4 use a simple resistor divider to provide a pseudo centre rail, and Fig.8.2b shows a zener split supply.

Fortunately the current flowing in the centre rail is often considerably smaller than the supply rail, and most of the current flowing out of the positive rail returns on the negative rail.

This means that the centre rail can often be provided by a simple resistor divider as Fig.8.5a. Capacitors C1 and C2 decouple any transient high currents. Higher centre rail currents (up to 15mA) can be obtained by using a unity gain Op Amp buffer as Fig.8.5c. Higher currents can be obtained by using one of the self biasing Audio power amplifier ICs. These automatically bias the output to the centre point of the supply rails. A typical circuit is shown on Fig.8.5b. It should be noted that the use of an audio amplifier IC is probably more expensive than buying a transformer with two second-

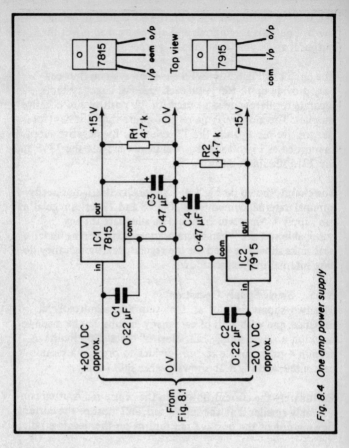

Fig. 8.4 One amp power supply

aries, and Fig.8.5b, whilst technically feasible, is not economically justifiable!

8.2.6 DC to DC Converters

Op Amps are often used with logic, so there is frequently a need for a 5V, +15V, and −15V supply together. This is often best obtained by using a single 5 volt power supply and a DC to DC converter operating off the 5 volt supply to provide the Op Amp rails. Although the DC to DC converter can be home built, encapsulated units are available at a very reason-

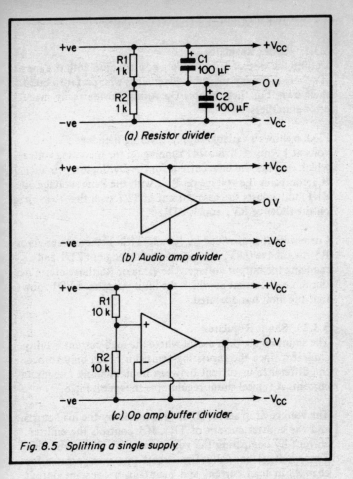

(a) Resistor divider

(b) Audio amp divider

(c) Op amp buffer divider

Fig. 8.5 Splitting a single supply

able price (around £5 at the time of writing). The use of these converters with a commercial 5 volt supply is often cheaper than building a three rail power supply.

8.3   POWER SUPPLIES USING OP AMPS

8.3.1   Series Regulator
Despite the ease of power supply construction with the special ICs there are many rugged individualists who prefer to build their own. For these people Op Amps provide ready made error amplifiers.

Fig.8.6 shows a variable supply covering the range 5V to 24 volts at 1 Amp. IC1 is a 741 running on the incoming voltage, which supplies the base current for the Darlington pair TR1. IC1 compares the voltage on RV1 with the Zener voltage on ZD1, and adjusts the base current of TR1 such that the voltage on the slider of RV1 equals ZD1.

Current limit is provided by R5 and TR2. If the voltage across R5 rises above 0.8V, TR2 turns on shorting out ZD1 and reducing the output voltage. The value of R5 thus determines the value of current at which the limit operates. LED1 shows that the limit has operated.

8.3.2   Shunt Regulator
The shunt regulator is useful where the load current is fairly constant, since the regulating transistor needs only to pass the difference in current between minimum and maximum current. A typical shunt regulator is shown on Fig.8.7.

The voltage drop across R2 is determined by the load current and the emitter current of TR1. IC1 controls the emitter current by comparing the voltage on RV1 slider with the Zener voltage on ZD1. The circuit thus compensates for changes in load current and maintains a constant output voltage.

If the load current is fairly constant, the current through TR1 is quite small and low power transistors can be used. Note, however, that the dissipation in TR1 rises with decreasing load, and is at maximum when the load is removed. Shunt regulators should therefore be switched between the regulator and transformer/rectifier if a low power transistor is used for

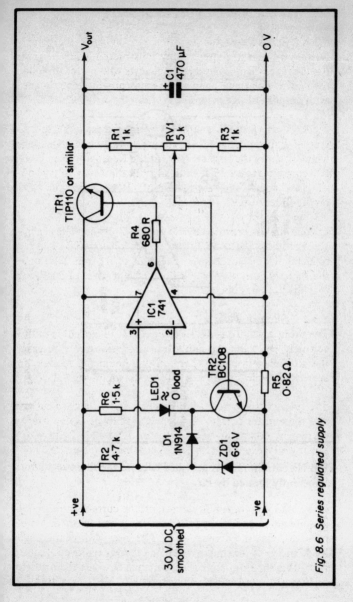

Fig. 8.6 Series regulated supply

149

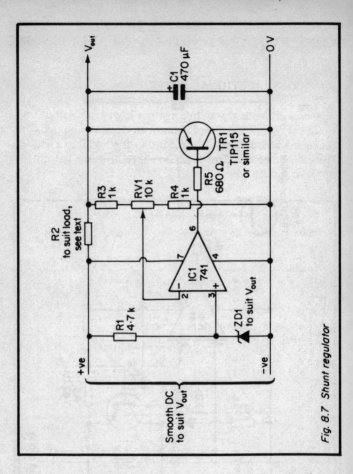

Fig. 8.7 Shunt regulator

TR1. No current limit is provided because the shunt regulator is inherently limited by R2.

CHAPTER 9
CONSTRUCTIONAL NOTES AND FAULT FINDING

9.1 CONSTRUCTIONAL NOTES

The most convenient way to construct any circuit with ICs is to use 0.1″ pitch stripboard. Almost all electronic components (including DIL packages) are made on a 0.1″ grid, so a neat layout can be made. Fig.9.1 shows a layout for the thermometer of section 6.8.

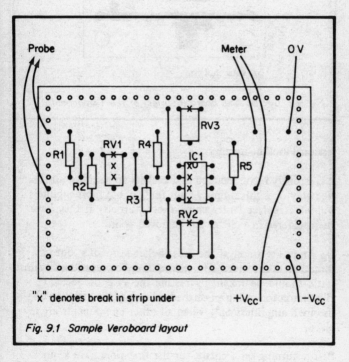

Fig. 9.1 Sample Veroboard layout

An alternative method is to use a specially designed Op Amp PCB available from many suppliers. Typical of these is the board produced by RS Components shown on Fig.9.2. This allows almost any Op Amp circuit to be constructed in a pro-

151

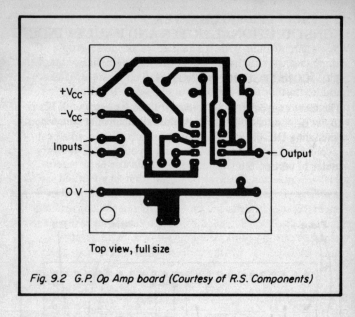

Fig. 9.2 G.P. Op Amp board (Courtesy of R.S. Components)

fessional looking manner.

It is strongly recommended that sockets are used for all ICs. Not only does this simplify fault finding, but most suppliers will NOT replace faulty chips under warranty if they have been soldered in a circuit and removed again.

Op Amps are amongst the most bullet proof ICs, but care should be taken with FET versions. Simple precautions against static should be taken, by resting the PCB on earthed aluminium foil, using an earthed soldering iron and inserting the FET amplifiers only when all other components are in place.

Before turning on a circuit for the first time have a quick visual check for solder splashes, uncut tracks and chips in the wrong way round. We all do it from time to time!

152

9.2 FAULT FINDING

When a circuit built with ICs fails to work, most people assume that the chip has failed. It should be emphasised that faulty ICs are very, very rare, and dead chips are usually murdered rather than die of natural causes. It follows that replacement of ICs as a first step in fault finding is not recommended, as it could easily lead to the demise of another set of chips.

The first stage of fault finding should always be a careful visual examination, even on a circuit that has worked previously. Points to check are dry joints, shorting components, cracked tracks and the like. On a newly constructed circuit check for solder splashes, uncut tracks and easily made errors like putting a link one hole out or a diode wrong way round. (A common mistake is putting DIL ICs in wrong way round!)

If a visual inspection reveals nothing, its time to get out a multimeter (all electronic engineers should possess a meter, however humble!). First check the supplies for both presence and stability. If these are correct, check the supplies on all the ICs (positive on pin 7, negative on pin 4 on most 8 pin Op Amps).

The next thing to check is the voltage at the inputs and output. These will vary according to the actual circuit, but as a general rule in all Op Amp circuits using feedback, the voltages at the two inputs should be the same. In circuits with high value resistances, the meter may load the circuit, so a meter should be used with a modicum of common sense.

If the voltages do not reveal the fault, now is the time to change ICs. This will be simplified if sockets have been used as advised earlier. If the Op Amp tester of section 6.14 has been built, the removed Op Amp can be tested. If not, another Op Amp can be substituted.

It should be noted that many circuits with adjustments for

zeroing, gain etc. can easily be maladjusted to the point where an output sits permanently at one or the other supply rail, or refuses to budge from zero. Potentiometers are invariably delivered with the slider at one end or other. It is good practice to set them at mid range before turning a circuit on for the first time.